The Way To Pass

Maths

Level 5

The Way to Pass
National Curriculum
Maths
Level 5

Geoff Buckwell

VERMILION
LONDON

First published in 1994

3 5 7 9 10 8 6 4 2

Text copyright © Rockhopper 1994

The moral right of the Author has been asserted
in accordance with the Copyright, Designs and
Patents Act, 1988.

First published in the United Kingdom in 1994
by Vermilion
an imprint of Ebury Press
Random House, 20 Vauxhall Bridge Road,
London SW1V 2SA

Random House Australia (Pty) Limited
20 Alfred Street, Milsons Point, Sydney,
New South Wales 2061, Australia

Random House New Zealand Limited
18 Poland Road, Glenfield,
Auckland 10, New Zealand

Random House South Africa (Pty) Limited
PO Box 337, Bergvlei, South Africa

Random House UK Limited Reg. No. 954009

Editor: Alison Wormleighton
Design: Jerry Goldie Graphic Design

A CIP catalogue record for this book
is available from the British Library

ISBN 0-09-178118-3

Typeset by AFS Image Setters Ltd, Glasgow
Printed in Great Britain by Butler & Tanner Ltd,
London and Frome

Foreword

Welcome to THE WAY TO PASS NATIONAL CURRICULUM MATHS LEVEL 5. I want to tell you why I have put together this series of books, along with a team of teachers, advisers and examiners.

A lot of people don't enjoy Maths because they're frightened of it. I can understand how frightening it can be because I've been scared of it myself at times: maybe the teacher goes through the work a little too quickly for you, maybe there are too many children in your class, maybe you're not the best at Maths in your class. All of these reasons can make Maths seem impossible. What I have learned through the years is that the more help you have and the longer you spend on something, the more likely you are to get over any difficulties.

Whatever you might think about school, and about Maths in particular, there is no doubt that Maths and English are the two most important subjects for you to do well in. If you understand most of what you're taught, you are set for a brighter future, being able to do some of the things you've always wanted to. The WAY TO PASS series can help you through secondary school, making the subjects you're taught a little more understandable and interesting, making your tests easier and helping you to get the best grades possible.

All of the books are based around work for you to do at home. Most of the explanations will have been covered in classes at school and so you won't want to wade through pages and pages of more explanations. That is why in each section we give you a concise list of the main things you need to know, and then work through exercises to practise each one.

This completely new range of books has been organised so that, if you want to, you can follow the already successful VIDEO CLASS videos covering the same subjects/levels. All of the book sections work together neatly with the video sections so that you have a complete course at your fingertips. Alternatively, the books can be used on their own, without the videos.

I certainly hope that this series will make Maths and English more approachable and slightly friendlier than they were before. Remember, you must follow what is taught in school and do as many exercises as you can—the more practice you get, the better you will be.

Carol Vorderman

Contents

The National Curriculum

The National Curriculum sets targets for pupils of all abilities from age 5 to 16, specifying what they should know, understand and be able to do at each stage of their education. It is divided into four **Key Stages**: Key Stage 1 (age 5–7), Key Stage 2 (age 7–11), Key Stage 3 (age 11–14) and Key Stage 4 (age 14–16).

The GCSE examinations are the main way of assessing children's progress at the end of Key Stage 4 (age 16). Prior to that, at the end of Key Stages 1, 2 and 3 (i.e. at ages 7, 11 and 14), pupils will be assessed in two ways: continuous assessment by the teachers and national tests, in which children will be asked to perform specific tasks relevant to the subject. Children will take the tests in English and Maths at age 7, 11 and 14 and in Science at age 11 and 14. These three subjects are at the heart of the National Curriculum and are known as the **core subjects**.

By combining the test results and continuous assessment, a teacher will be able to determine the **Level** a child has reached in each of these subjects. Different children at the same Key Stage may achieve widely varying results and therefore different Levels.

An average child will probably move up one Level every two years or so, starting at Level 1 at the age of 5. This means that at the end of Key Stage 1 (age 7) they may reach Level 2, at the end of Key Stage 2 (age 11) Level 4 and at the end of Key Stage 3 (age 14) Level 5 or 6. Slower learners could be a Level or two lower in one or more subjects, while some children could be two or even three Levels higher. Level 10 is the highest, but only a few children will achieve this Level.

The books for Levels 4, 5 and 6 in THE WAY TO PASS series are based on National Curriculum requirements for each of those Levels and are suitable for the secondary school child aged 11 to 14. They will serve as a valuable back-up to a child's classwork and homework and provide an excellent preparation for the tests at the end of Key Stage 3.

Introduction

The WAY TO PASS books for Key Stage 3 are written to provide you with that extra support you will need at home while preparing for the National Curriculum tests. This book is aimed at Maths Level 5 pupils. (If you are not sure which Level you are working towards, your teacher will be able to tell you.)

Although there are lots of facts you have to learn (listed under **Things You Need to Know** at the beginning of each section of the book) most of your time should be spent actually working out problems. In **How to Do It** in each section, there are worked examples. As you do these, cover up the solutions to check you understand that particular topic. When you feel confident, try the **Do It Yourself** questions in that section. You'll find the **Answers** near the end of the book.

Some of the exercises have been marked with a picture of a calculator. This means you should use a calculator to do it. However, in the exercises that have a picture of a calculator with a cross through it, you must not use one. (It is very important in the real tests that you show your full working, including carry digits, in this type of question. Failure to do so would mean you'd score no marks for that question.)

The numbering system used in the book makes it easy for you to concentrate on whatever topics you feel you most need to revise. Each topic within a section has a number, which identifies that topic throughout the section. Thus, in Section 1, no. 5 of Things You Need to Know covers negative numbers; then exercises 5a and 5b of How to Do It show you how to answer questions involving negative numbers; and finally you can check how well you understand negative numbers with exercises 5a, 5b and 5c of Do It Yourself.

Many questions in the National Curriculum tests will cover more than one topic. You should pay particular attention in this book to the work in sections 9 and 11 on shape and in section 13 on algebra.

At the end of the book there is a **Sample Test Paper** made up of the type of questions you will be given, followed by solutions. It should take you about 60 minutes to do. If this were a real Key Stage 3 test, you would need to get about three-quarters of the answers correct to be successful at Level 5.

Don't leave your revision until the last minute before your Key Stage 3 test. Remember, the more you practise, the better you will cope with it.

1

Working with Numbers

Things You Need to Know

1 How to multiply and divide without using a calculator.

2 How to multiply and divide by 10, 100, 200 etc. without using a calculator.

3 That a **factor** of a number divides exactly into that number. For example, 5 and 6 are factors of 30 (there are others). A **prime number** has no factors other than 1 and the number itself. The first few prime numbers are 2, 3, 5, 7, 11, . . . (Notice that 1 is not regarded as a prime factor.)

Thus, 5 is not only a factor of 30 but actually a **prime factor** of 30.

The **multiples** of 4 for example, are 4, 8, 12, 16, . . . (the 'four times table' and its extension).

4 **Powers** or **index** numbers are used to abbreviate things like $3 \times 3 \times 3 \times 3$ which can be written 3^4 (we say three to the power 4).

> *Notes:* (i) Power 2 is the same as squared.
> (ii) Power 3 is the same as cubed.
> (iii) 4^1 is simply 4.
> (iv) $5^0 = 1$ (any number to the power zero is 1).

The reverse of squaring is square rooting ($\sqrt{}$). So

$\sqrt{36} = 6$ because $6^2 = 36$.

The reverse of cubing is cube rooting ($\sqrt[3]{}$). Hence

$\sqrt[3]{64} = 4$ because $4^3 = 64$.

5 **Negative** numbers are numbers that are less than zero. For example, $9 - 11 = (-2)$: negative 2. Remember, the $-$ in -2 means a **negative number**. The $-$ sign in $9 - 11$ means **subtract**.
    The rules for multiplying and dividing are given in the following table:

$\times$ or $\div$	Positive	Negative
Positive	Positive	Negative
Negative	Negative	Positive

How to Do It

1 **a** Work out 423×54 without a calculator, showing all of your working.

Solution
Make sure that you keep the columns of the numbers lined up. Always put the smaller number underneath.

```
        4  2  3
   ×       5  4 ——— (i)      (i)  multiply by 4
      1  6  9₁ 2
   2  1₁ 1₁ 5  0 ——— (ii)    (ii) multiply by 50
   2  2  8₁ 4  2
```

Hence $423 \times 54 = 22\,842$.

11

b Work out $336 \div 14$ without a calculator, showing all of your working.

Solution
Method 1

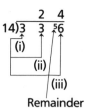

Remainder

(i)   14 does not divide into 3

(ii) 14 divides into 33 twice, leaving a remainder 5

(iii) 14 divides into 56 exactly 4 times

So $336 \div 14 = 24$.

Method 2

$$
\begin{array}{r}
2\ \ 4 \\
\hline
14)3\ \ 3\ \ 6 \\
2\ \ 8 \longleftarrow\quad 2 \times 14 \\
\hline
5\ \ 6 \\
5\ \ 6 \longleftarrow\quad 4 \times 14 \\
\hline
0 \longleftarrow\ \text{remainder}
\end{array}
$$

'Choose whichever method you are used to'

2 a Carry out the following calculations without the use of a calculator:

(i) 26×1000 (ii) 42×200
(iii) $86\,000 \div 100$ (iv) $2400 \div 300$

Solution

(i) 26 can be written 26.00. Multiplying by 100 moves the decimal point two places to the *right* to give 2600, so

$$26 \times 100 = 2600$$

(ii) First find $42 \times 2 = 84$. Then $84 \times 100 = 8400$ as in part (i). So

$$42 \times 200 = 8400$$

(iii) Since 86 000 is really 86 000.0, if we divide by 100 the decimal place moves two places to the *left* to become 860.00 So

$$86\,000 \div 100 = 860$$

'Long division can always be checked by multiplying back'

(iv) First divide 2400 by 3 to give 800. Then

$$800 \div 100 = 8$$
$$So \ 2400 \div 300 = 8$$

b An aeroplane flies at a speed of 300 km/h for 4 hours between two airports A and B.
  (i) How far apart are the two airports?
  (ii) The plane returns from B to A in 5 hours. What is the average speed for the return journey?

Solution

(i) The distance travelled = speed × time = 300 × 4 = 1200 km
(ii) To find the average speed on the return journey, you need to work out 1200 ÷ 5. The quickest way to divide by 5 without a calculator is to divide by 10 (the answer is now too small), and then double the answer:

$$1200 \div 10 \quad = 120$$
$$Average \ speed \ = 120 \times 2 = 240 \ km/h$$

'Speed =
  distance'
  time

3a Find all the factors of 36. Which of these factors are also prime factors?

Solution

Don't forget 1 and 36 will be factors. Work through, starting at 1 and list all the numbers that divide exactly into 36. The numbers are:

1, 2, 3, 4, 6, 9, 12, 18, 36

The prime factors are 2 and 3.

b Write down the first seven multiples of 6 and the first seven multiples of 5. State the smallest number (called the lowest common multiple) that 6 and 5 divide into exactly.

*'Lowest
common
multiple is
abbreviated
LCM'*

Solution

The multiples of 5 are: 5   10   15   20   25 $\boxed{30}$ 35
The multiples of 6 are: 6   12   18   24 $\boxed{30}$ 36   42
The *smallest* number that appears in both sets of numbers is 30.

4 a Work out 4^5.

Solution
Method 1

$$4^5 = 4 \times 4 \times 4 \times 4 \times 4$$

Hence using the calculator

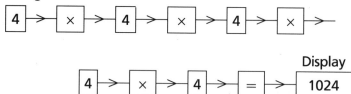

Method 2
If you have a power button $\boxed{x^y}$ on your calculator, this can be done in fewer key strokes.

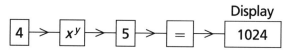

b Find: (i) $\sqrt{81}$ (ii) $\sqrt[3]{27}$ (iii) $\sqrt{8.4}$ (iv) $\sqrt[3]{40}$

Solution

(i) We remember that $9 \times 9 = 81$ so $\sqrt{81} = 9$.
(ii) We remember that $3 \times 3 \times 3 = 27$ so $\sqrt[3]{27} = 3$.
(iii) There is no exact answer to this, so you will have to use a calculator:

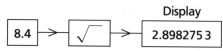

Hence $\sqrt{8.4} = 2.898$ (three decimal places).

(iv) In order to do this part, you will need a scientific calculator with a cube root button $\boxed{\sqrt[3]{}}$.

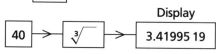

So $\sqrt[3]{40} = 3.420$ (three decimal places).

'For some calculators, you may need the $\boxed{INV}$ or $\boxed{SHIFT}$ or $\boxed{2nd\,f}$ button for the cube root'

5 **a** Work out the following without a calculator:
   (i) $8+(-3)$ (ii) $(-3)-(-7)$
   (iii) $(-2)\times(-16)$ (iv) $(-12)\div4$ (v) $(-6)+(-3)$

'The number line is very useful in this type of problem'

Solution

(i) To add (-3) you move to the left. Hence

$$8+(-3)=5$$

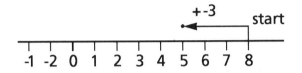

(ii) To subtract (-7) you move to the right. Hence

$$(-3)-(-7)=4$$

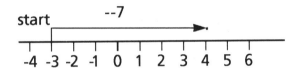

(iii) Negative $\times$ negative $=$ positive. So

$$(-2)\times(-16)=32$$

(iv) Negative $\div$ positive $=$ negative. Therefore

$$(-12)\div4=(-3)$$

(v) To add (-3) you move to the left. So

$$(-6)+(-3)=(-9)$$

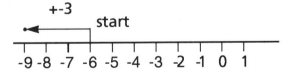

b Use a calculator to work out the following:
   (i) $12-(-5)$ (ii) $(-41)\times(-37)$
   (iii) $120\div(-24)$

Solution

The button $\boxed{+/-}$ is used to enter a negative number. You press this after entering the digits.

(i)

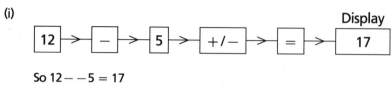

So $12 - -5 = 17$

(ii)

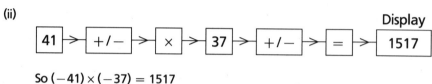

So $(-41) \times (-37) = 1517$

(iii)

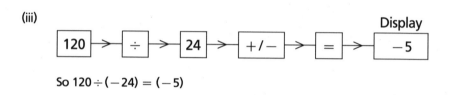

So $120 \div (-24) = (-5)$

'Read your calculator instruction booklet carefully'

Do It Yourself

1 Work out, showing all your working:

    (i) 26×31 (ii) 121×14
   (iii) $896 \div 16$ (iv) $1190 \div 14$
    (v) 387×24 (vi) $1020 \div 15$

2 Write down the answers to the following, without using a calculator:

    (i) $23 \times 10\,000$ (ii) 108×200
   (iii) $490\,000 \div 100$ (iv) $35\,000 \div 70$
    (v) 222×200 (vi) $408\,000 \div 400$

3a Find all factors of the following numbers:

    (i) 12   (ii) 28   (iii) 40
   (iv) 19   (v) 25   (vi) 50

b What is the smallest number that 6 and 8 divide into exactly?

4 Use a calculator if necessary to work out the following:

(i) 2^3 (ii) 5^3 (iii) 4^4

(iv) $\sqrt{144}$ (v) $\sqrt{169}$ (vi) 2^6

(vii) $4^2 \times 2^3$ (viii) $\sqrt[3]{27}$ (ix) $\sqrt[3]{125}$

(x) 10^3 (xi) 6^0 (xii) 40^1

(xiii) $\sqrt{67}$ (xiv) $\sqrt[3]{9.5}$ (xv) $\sqrt{0.833}$

5a Work out the following:

(i) $2\frac{1}{2} \times (-4)$ (ii) $(-5\frac{1}{2}) + 12$ (iii) $24 \div (-6)$

(iv) $(-8) \div (-16)$ (v) $11 - (-3)$ (vi) $(-12) - 4$

(vii) $8 - (-3) + (-5)$

b The level of the tide is marked on the side of a jetty by a scale. The average tide height is at zero. At high tide, the reading is 1.8 m, and at low tide the reading is −0.8 m. What is the difference in levels between high and low tide?

c The temperature at a place in Iceland was 5 degrees below zero while the temperature at London was 18 degrees above zero. How much warmer was it in London?

2 Number Patterns

Things You Need to Know

1 A **number pattern** is a sequence of numbers in which it is possible to predict the next number from previous numbers in the pattern. The early numbers in the pattern enable us to discover the pattern and therefore predict later numbers in the pattern.

Certain number sequences have special names:

(i) 1, 2, 3, 4, . . .   natural numbers
(ii) 2, 4, 6, 8, . . .   even numbers
(iii) 1, 3, 5, 7, . . .   odd numbers
(iv) 1, 4, 9, 16, . . .   square numbers

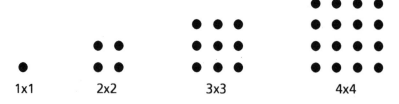

1x1   2x2   3x3   4x4

(v) 1, 3, 6, 10, . . .   triangular numbers

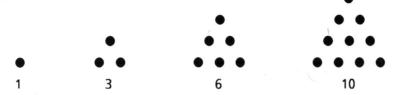

1   3   6   10

Numbers can be predicted from written instructions, or simple flow charts.

2 How to investigate a number sequence using a computer program. Also, how to write a simple program that will generate a given sequence of numbers.

How to Do It

1 a Look at this matchstick pattern.

Complete the following table:

Number of matches M	3	5	7		
Number of triangles T	1	2	3	4	5

The flow chart below shows part of the rule for getting M from T. Fill in the missing box.

$T \rightarrow$ ⎡rule?⎤ $\rightarrow$ ⎡$+1$⎤ $\rightarrow M$

Solution
M increased by *two* each time, and so the missing numbers are 9 and 11.
    If you take 1 from the values of M, you get 2, 4, 6, 8, . . . These values are double the value of T. Hence the missing rule is ⎡$\times 2$⎤.

'If you can form a number of snooker balls in the shape of a triangle, then that number is a triangular number'

'Try to invent your own matchstick patterns'

'You can make a whole variety of number patterns by following different written instructions'

b The following number pattern is very famous, and is called the Fibonacci series:

$$1, 1, 2, 3, 5, \ldots$$

Each number is found by adding together the two previous numbers in the series. Work out the tenth number in this series.

Solution

$1+1 = 2$	$1+2 = 3$	$2+3 = 5$	$3+5 = 8$
$5+8 = 13$	$8+13 = 21$	$13+21 = 34$	$21+34 = 55$

The sequence is

$$1, 1, 2, 3, 5, 8, 13, 21, 34, 55$$

Hence the tenth number is 55.

2 a A number sequence is generated by the following computer program:

```
10  FOR N = 1 TO 10
20  PRINT 2 * N + 3
30  NEXT N
40 END
```

Work out the sequence it produces. Describe the sequence.

Solution
Lines 10 and 30 tell you to repeat a calculation with

$$N = 1, 2, 3, 4, 5, 6, 7, 8, 9, 10$$

Line 20 tells you to write down the value of $2N+3$ for these numbers. For example,

$$N = 1, \quad \text{Print } 2 \times 1 + 3 = 5$$
$$N = 2, \quad \text{Print } 2 \times 2 + 3 = 7$$

The sequence you get is

$$5, 7, 9, 11, 13, 15, 17, 19, 21, 23$$

*'Remember that in BASIC * means multiply'*

The best way to describe these numbers is 'odd numbers from 5 to 23 inclusive'.

b Design a simple program that will print the following number sequence:
20, 17, 14, 11, 8, 5, 2.

Solution

First of all you need to see that the numbers *decrease* by 3 each time. This means that the numbers are related to multiples of 3. In computer notation, this is written $3*N$.

Next, notice that there are seven numbers in the sequence, and so you need a statement that will count from 1 to 7. This is FOR N = 1 TO 7. Since the first number is 20, and the numbers are decreasing, you need to keep subtracting multiples of 3 from 23. This is achieved by the statement $23 - 3*N$.

The complete program becomes

```
10  FOR N = 1 TO 7
15  PRINT 23 − 3*N
20  NEXT N
25  END
```

'Notice you need 23 and not 20 in line 15'

Do It Yourself

1 a A sequence of numbers begins as follows:

2, 7, 17, ,37, . . .

The rule for continuing the sequence is 'double the last number and add 3'. What are the next three numbers in the sequence?

b A row of squares is made using matchsticks:

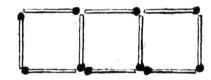

If the pattern continues in this way, complete the following table. (One has been done for you.)

Number of squares	1	2	3	4	5
Number of matches		7			

Describe the numbers in the bottom row of the table.

c A number sequence is formed by doubling each number and adding 5. If the first number in the sequence is 7, what is the tenth number in the sequence?

d Look at the following dot patterns:

    (i) how many dots are in the first pattern?
    (ii) How many dots are in the second pattern?
    (iii) How many dots are in the third pattern?
    (iv) If this series of patterns continues, explain how to find the number of dots in the rest of the sequence.

2 **a** Write down the number sequences generated by the following computer programs:

    (i)
```
 5 FOR N = 1 TO 6
10 PRINT N * 4 + 8
15 NEXT N
20 END
```

    (ii)
```
10 FOR T = 1 TO 8
20 PRINT 16 − 3 * T
30 NEXT T
40 END
```

    (iii)
```
100 FOR M = 1 TO 10
110 PRINT M * M + M
120 NEXT M
130 END
```

'Try to run these programs on a computer if you have access to one'

b Write simple programs which give the following number sequences:
    (i) 1, 3, 5, 7, 9, 11, 13
    (ii) 10, 8, 6, 4, 2, 0
    (iii) 2, 5, 10, 17, 26

Fractions, Percentages and Ratios

3

Things You Need to Know

1 A **fraction** is a *part* of something. It is written

$$\frac{\text{numerator}}{\text{denominator}}$$

For example, in the fraction $\frac{3}{5}$, 3 is the **numerator** and 5 is the **denominator**. (Any fraction in this style can be called a **vulgar** fraction.)

Fractions with equal values such as $\frac{3}{5}$ and $\frac{6}{10}$ are referred to as **equivalent** fractions. A fraction can be simplified by cancelling. So

$$\frac{24}{36} = \frac{24^2}{36_3} = \frac{2}{3} \quad \text{(divide top and bottom by 12—we say cancel by 12)}$$

An **improper** fraction is one in which the numerator is bigger than the denominator. (The top is bigger than the bottom.) For example, $\frac{11}{5}$ is an improper fraction.

A fraction can be changed into a decimal by dividing the numerator by the denominator. So

$$\frac{5}{8} = 5 \div 8 = 0.625 \quad \text{(by calculator)}$$

2 The percentage sign (%) means 'out of 100'. So 25% means 25 out of 100, or as a fraction

$$\frac{25}{100} = \frac{1}{4} \quad \text{(cancel by 25)}$$

A fraction or decimal can be changed into a percentage if you multiply by 100.

3 A ratio such as 4 : 1 means there is four times as much of one quantity as another.

A ratio can sometimes be simplified, so that 8 : 2 is the same as 4 : 1.

How to Do It

1 **a** Shade $\frac{2}{3}$ of this shape, so that no square is completely shaded.

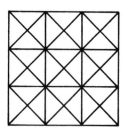

Solution

The shape consists of 36 small triangles. You need to find a fraction equivalent to $\frac{2}{3}$ which has 36 on the bottom line. So

$$\frac{2}{3} = \frac{2 \times 12}{3 \times 12} = \frac{24}{36}$$

'Top and bottom lines are multiplied by 12'

You can now shade 24 triangles making sure that no square is fully shaded. One possible solution is shown alongside (there are others).

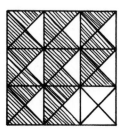

b Change $\frac{11}{5}$ into a mixed number.

Solution
$\frac{11}{5}$ means 11 lots of $\frac{1}{5}$. But 5 lots of $\frac{1}{5}$ make one, so if you divide 11 by 5, you get 2 remainder 1. Hence $\frac{11}{5}$ is 2 and $\frac{1}{5}$, i.e. $2\frac{1}{5}$.

'Note $2\frac{1}{5}$ is not $\frac{21}{5}$'

c Find $\frac{2}{5}$ of £8.50.

Solution
Method 1
The word 'of' in mathematics means multiply; so

$$\frac{2}{5} \text{ of } £8.50 = \frac{2}{5} \times 8.50$$
$$= \frac{2 \times 8.50}{5} = \frac{17}{5} = 3.40$$

Hence $\frac{2}{5}$ of £8.50 = £3.40.

'Choose whichever method you prefer'

Method 2
First find $\frac{1}{5}$ of £8.50 by dividing 8.5 by 5 to give 1.7. Remember this is really £1.70. So $\frac{2}{5}$ will be

$$2 \times £1.70 = £3.40$$

2a Change the following into percentages:
(i) $\frac{3}{4}$ (ii) $\frac{5}{8}$ (iii) 0.164

Solution
To change a fraction or decimal to a percentage, you multiply by 100:

(i) $\frac{3}{4} \times 100 = \frac{300}{4} = 75\%$

(ii) $\frac{5}{8} \times 100 = \frac{500}{8} = 62.5\%$ (by calculator)

(iii) $0.164 \times 100 = 16.4\%$

'The decimal point has moved two places to the right'

b In a survey of 80 households, it was found that 45 of them had a video recorder. Express this as a percentage.

Solution
45 out of 80 can be written $\frac{45}{80}$. This fraction can now be changed to a percentage.

Method 1

$$\frac{45}{80} \times 100 = \frac{4500}{80} = 56.25\% \quad \text{(by calculator)}$$

Method 2

$$\frac{45}{\underset{4}{80}} \times \overset{5}{100} \quad \text{(by cancelling)}$$

This equals

$$\frac{45}{4} \times 5 = \frac{225}{4} = 56.25\%$$

Method 3
By calculator

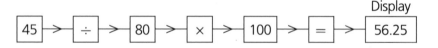

c Peter and Viv are travelling to work by bus. The fare for a single journey is £1.20. The fares are about to increase by 15%. If they make a return journey five days a week, how much extra will each person's fares be per week?

Solution
To find 15% of £1.20, you work out

$$\frac{15}{100} \times £1.20 = £0.15 \times 1.20$$

$$= £0.18 \quad \text{(by calculator)}$$

They make 10 single journeys each week, hence the weekly increase is

$$10 \times £0.18 = £1.80$$

3 Black and white beads are threaded on to a fine cord in order to make a necklace. They are put on in the ratio

Black : white = 3 : 2

If each necklace has 30 beads, how many of each colour are needed?

Solution

3 : 2 means that for every 2 white beads, 3 black beads are needed. Hence the beads can be grouped in units of $2 + 3 = 5$. (Always add together the two numbers in the ratio.) Now divide the total 30 by 5

$30 \div 5 = 6$

We deduce there are 6 groups.

So the number of black beads $= 6 \times 3 = 18$
and the number of white beads $= 6 \times 2 = 12$

Do It Yourself

1 a The diagram shows a large field marked out for growing various vegetables. Work out in its simplest form the fraction of the field used to grow:
 (i) carrots;
 (ii) peas.

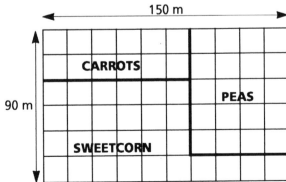

b Change the following improper fractions into mixed numbers:

(i) $\frac{8}{5}$ (ii) $\frac{15}{4}$ (iii) $\frac{23}{2}$ iv) $\frac{19}{3}$

c Change the following mixed numbers into improper fractions:

(i) $1\frac{4}{5}$ (ii) $1\frac{5}{8}$ (iii) $2\frac{3}{4}$ (iv) $5\frac{1}{2}$

2 a How much will a shirt originally priced at £20 cost in the sale?

b Change into a percentage:

(i) $\frac{2}{5}$ (ii) $\frac{3}{4}$ (iii) $\frac{7}{8}$ (iv) 0.812

c British Rail stated that of 80 journeys between two stations, 63 had arrived more or less on time. What percentage of the trains had arrived late?

d Danielle had just taken a science test. She was told that if she scored more than 70% she could go into the top set. Her mark was 54 out of 75. Did she get promoted? Show your working.

3 a Peter, aged 8, and Joseph, aged 6, were given £28 to be divided between them in the ratio of their ages. How much did each one get?

b Red gums and black gums are mixed in the ratio 3 : 2. How many black gums should you get in a box which holds 25 of these gums?

Estimating and Approximating

Things You Need to Know

1　How to round a number to a given level of accuracy.
　　How to round a number to a given number of decimal places (count to the right of the decimal point).
　　How to round a number to a given number of significant figures.

2　How to solve problems by trial and improvement methods. In particular, how to find a square root.

How to Do It

1ᵃ　Round the following measurements as required:
　　(i)　8.6 m to the nearest metre;
　　(ii)　4.34 cm to the nearest millimetre;
　　(iii)　863 to the nearest 100.

Solution

If you find these ideas difficult, try to visualise a scale and look for the point that it is nearest to:

(i) Clearly the answer is *nearest* to 9 m.

(ii) The small divisions are the millimetres, and so we ask ourselves, 'Is 4.34 cm closer to 4.3 cm or 4.4 cm?' We conclude it is *nearer* to 4.3 cm.

(iii) This is *nearest* to 900.

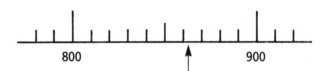

b Round the following numbers to one decimal place:
  (i) 8.634   (ii) 7.45   (iii) 8.07   (iv) 0.0362

> **'Decimal places are counted to the right of the decimal point'**

Solution

(i) 8.6¦34   6 is followed by 3 and so the 6 remains unaltered

  8.364 = 8.6 to one decimal place

(ii) 7.4¦5   4 is followed by 5 and so the 4 rounds up to 5

  7.45 = 7.5 to one decimal place   (abbreviate to 1 d.p.)
    = 7.5   (1 d.p.)

(iii) 8.0¦7   0 is followed by 7 and so the 0 rounds up to 1

  8.07 = 8.1   (1 d.p.)

(iv) 0.0¦362   0 is followed by 3 and so the 0 remains unaltered

  0.0362 = 0.0   (1 d.p.)

c Round the following numbers to two significant figures:
(i) 493   (ii) 0.048 73   (iii) 4.093

Solution
Remember that significant figures are always counted from the first digit that is not a zero.

(i) 49 ¦ 3   9 is followed by 3 and so remains unaltered

$\qquad$ 493 = 490 to two significant figures   (abbreviate to 2 s.f.)

(ii) 0.048 ¦ 73   8 is followed by 7 and so rounds up to 9

$\qquad$ 0.048 73 = 0.049   (2 s.f.)

(iii) 4.0 ¦ 93   0 is followed by 9 and so rounds up to 1

$\qquad$ 4.093 = 4.1   (2 s.f.)

2

a Use trial and improvement to find the square root of 44 correct to two decimal places.

Solution
You need to have some idea of the answer. Now $\sqrt{36} = 6$ and $\sqrt{49} = 7$. So $\sqrt{44}$ must lie between 6 and 7.

(i)	Try 6.5	$6.5^2 = 42.25$	This is low
(ii)	Try 6.6	$6.6^2 = 43.56$	Slightly low
(iii)	Try 6.65	$6.65^2 = 44.2225$	Slightly high
(iv)	Try 6.64	$6.64^2 = 44.0896$	Slightly high
(v)	Try 6.63	$6.63^2 = 43.9569$	Slightly low

The last is the nearest to 44, and so $\sqrt{44} = 6.63$ to two decimal places.

b A farmer has 100 m of fencing to enclose a rectangular field measuring A m by B m. If the area of the field is 609 m² use a trial and improvement method to find A and B.

Solution
The perimeter is $2A + 2B$ and this must equal 100. So,
$$2A + 2B = 100$$
Divide by 2: $A + B = 50$
The area is 609, so $A \times B = 609$

'There are many starting points'

Try A = 24 and B = 26: then 24 × 26 = 624
Alter the numbers slightly: A = 23 and B = 27, so 23 × 27 = 621
The answer is moving in the right direction.
Try A = 21 and B = 29: 21 × 29 = 609
Hence A = 21 and B = 29. Is this the only solution?

Do It Yourself

1 a Carry out the following roundings:

    (i) 86.6 m to the nearest metre;
    (ii) 9.64 cm to the nearest millimetre;
    (iii) £9.24 to the nearest 50p;
    (iv) 32 871 to the nearest thousand;
    (v) $11\frac{5}{8}$ to the nearest $\frac{1}{2}$;
    (vi) £8.63 to the nearest 20p.

b Write down the following numbers correct to two decimal places:

    (i) 8.634   (ii) 5.094   (iii) 0.8996
    (iv) 1.0406   (v) 11.398   (vi) 0.999

c Write down the following numbers corrected to two significant figures:

    (i) 684   (ii) 8.63   (iii) 809
    (iv) 999   (v) 8.093   (vi) 16 325

2 a Jim has 64 m of fencing to enclose a rectangular field measuring A m by B m. If the area of the field is 975 m² use a trial and improvement method to find A and B. Explain carefully how you obtain the answers.

b Tim's calculator is broken, and the $\boxed{\sqrt{}}$ button does not work. Describe how he can find $\sqrt{60}$ accurately to two decimal places without using the square root button.

c Use a trial and improvement method to solve the equations:

    (i) $x^2 = 8$ (ii) $\dfrac{4x+1}{3x-2} = 6$

Give your answer in each case to two decimal places.

Units and Conversion Graphs

5

Things You Need to Know

1 The **metric system**:
   (i) units of length: millimetres (mm), centimetres (cm), metres (m), kilometres (km):

   1 cm = 10 mm   1 m = 100 cm   1 m = 1000 mm   1 km = 1000 m

   (ii) units of weight: grams (g), kilograms (kg), tonne:

   1 kg = 1000 g   1000 kg = 1 tonne

   (iii) units used to measure capacity (usually volume of liquids): millilitre (ml), cubic centimetre (cm³), litre (l), centilitre (cl):

   1 l = 1000 ml or 1 l = 100 cl   1 cl = 10 ml   1 ml = 1 cm³

2 The **imperial system**:
   (i) units of length:

   12 inches (in) = 1 foot (ft)
   1 yard (yd)   = 3 feet (ft)
   1 mile   = 1760 yds

'Measurements like 3 ft 5 in are sometimes written as 3'5"'

'A ml and a cm³ are the same because a litre occupies a cube measuring 10 cm × 10 cm × 10 cm'

(ii) units of weight:

16 ounces (oz) = 1 pound (lb)
14 pounds = 1 stone
20 stones = 1 hundredweight (cwt)
1 ton = 20 cwt

(iii) units of capacity:

1 gallon = 8 pints
20 fluid oz = 1 pint
1 fluid oz of water weighs 1 oz

'You will usually be told this information'

3 There are some approximate conversions between metric and imperial units that are quite useful:

1 lb = 450 g	20 fluid oz = 1 pint
1 kg = 2.2 lb	1 gallon = 4.5 l
1 ton = 1 tonne	1 l = 35 fluid oz

4 Different units can be converted by means of a **conversion graph**.

How to Do It

1 a (i) Convert 1.23 m into centimetres.
(ii) Convert 0.86 l into millilitres.
(iii) Convert 8643 g into kilograms.

Solution

(i) Metres → centimetres is the same as × 100, so

$$1.23 \times 100 = 123 \, cm$$

(ii) Litres → millilitres is the same as × 1000, so

$$0.86 \times 1000 = 860 \, ml$$

(iii) Grams → kilograms is the same as ÷ 1000, hence

$$8643 \div 1000 = 8.643 \, kg$$

b A can holds $\frac{1}{2}$ litre of cleaning liquid. If 75 ml are poured out into a beaker, how much is left in the can?

Solution

$\frac{1}{2}$ litre is $\frac{1}{2} \times 1000 = 500$ ml. The amount left is $500 - 75 = 425$ ml.

2 Amy measured the length of the garden with her mum's old tape measure. She wrote down these lengths: 1 yd, 2′ 6″, 1′ 8″, 2 yds 1′. She now has to add the lengths together to get the length of the garden. How long is it?

Solution

yds	ft	in
1	0	0
	2	6
	1	8
2	1	0
4	2	2
1	1	

(i) Remember 1 ft = 12 in, so

$$6'' + 8'' = 1' 2''$$

(ii) 3 ft = 1 yd, so

$$5\,ft = 1\,yd\,2\,ft$$

The length of the garden is 4 yds 2 ft 2 in.

'These units are very seldom used now'

3 Carry out the following approximate conversions:
   (i) 12 lb into kilograms   (ii) 200 fluid oz into litres
 (iii) 12 gallons into litres

Solution

  (i) Since 1 lb is approximately 450 g, 12 lb is

$$12 \times 450 = 5400\,g$$

   Now divide by 1000 to give 5.4 kg.
  (ii) Since 35 fluid oz is approximately 1 litre, then 200 fluid oz must be
     $200 \div 35 = 8.61$ litres
 (iii) 12 gallons $= 12 \times 4.5 = 54$ litres

4 At the time of writing, £1 can be exchanged for 2.4DM (Deutschmarks). Construct a graph that will allow you to change any amount up to £10. Use this graph, to change:

(i) £4.50 into DM   (ii) £8.20 into DM

(iii) 15DM into £   (iv) 150DM into £

Solution

Since £1 = 2.4DM, £10 × 2.4 = 24DM. This helps to choose the scale of the graph.

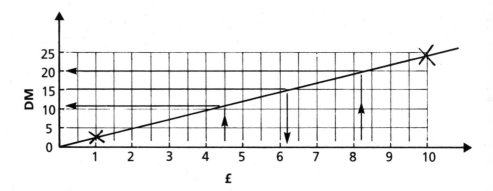

> *'You must plot two points and the origin to get the best line'*

Plot two points at (£1, 2.4DM) and (£10, 24DM). The graph must also go through (£0, 0DM).

(i) Read up from £4.50 to the line and across to the vertical scale to give roughly 11DM.

(ii) £8.20 is approximately 20DM.

(iii) Read across from 15DM to the line and down to the horizontal axis to give approximately £6.20.

(iv) 150DM does not appear in the scale, but it must be 10 × 15DM which is 10 × £6.20 = £62.

Do It Yourself

1a Complete the following:

    (i) 286 cm = . . . m   (ii) 58 mm = . . . cm

    (iii) 4.28 m = . . . cm   (iv) 0.4 m = . . . mm

    (v) 4800 g = . . . kg   (vi) 2.8 l = . . . ml

    (vii) 280 ml = . . . l   (viii) 4.82 kg = . . . g

2 Complete the following:

    (i) 1 ft 5 in = . . . in   (ii) $3\frac{1}{2}$ yards = . . . ft

    (iii) $2\frac{1}{4}$ gallons = . . . pints   (iv) 2 stone = . . . lb

    (v) 5 lb = . . . oz   (vi) 40 oz = . . . lb

    (vii) 4 pints = . . . gallons

    (viii) 64 in = . . . ft . . . in

3a Use the fact that 1 cm is 0.39 in to convert:

    (i) 6 cm into inches   (ii) 4 m into inches

b Use the fact that 1 kg = 2.2 lb to convert:

    (i) 8 kg into pounds   (ii) 10 lb into kilograms

4a The graph alongside converts £ sterling into American dollars ($).

Use the graph to convert:

    (i) £6.50 into dollars

    (ii) £28 into dollars

    (iii) $8.50 into £

    (iv) $100 into £

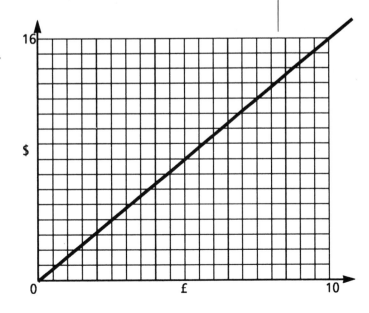

b Most people know that 0° Celsius is the same as 32° Fahrenheit, and 100° Celsius is the same as 212° Fahrenheit. On a sheet of graph paper, with a horizontal scale from $-10\,°C$ to $100\,°C$ and a vertical scale from $0\,°F$ to $212\,°F$, plot these two points and join them with a straight line. You have now constructed a conversion graph from °Celsius to °Fahrenheit. Use your graph to change:

    (i) 50 °C to °F   (ii) 85 °C to °F

    (iii) 20 °F to °C   (iv) 100 °F to °C

c Jenny wanted to make herself a conversion graph between gallons and litres. She used the fact that one gallon = 4.5 l. Draw a graph with vertical axis from 0 to 50 litres, and the horizontal axis from 0 to 10 gallons, using the information that she used. From the graph, find

    (i) How many litres are in $4\frac{1}{2}$ gallons.

    (ii) How many gallons there are in 220 litres.

    (iii) The cost of 1 gallon of petrol, which is priced at 50p per litre.

Measuring

6

Things You Need to Know

1 The choice of appropriate units is intended to avoid answers that contain too many zeros after the decimal point before the first digit (e.g. 0.0004 km) and answers that contain too many zeros in front of the decimal point (e.g. 20 000 mm).

2 If information is given to you in a variety of units, change all of them into the same units before making any calculations.

3 How to read a timetable.

CONTENTS

How to Do It

1
a Which unit would you think most suitable to use in measuring:
  (i)   your weight;
  (ii) the length of a football pitch;
  (iii) the thickness of a sheet of glass;
  (iv) the length of a shoe.

'Try measuring using a variety of units to get a feel for them.'

Solution

  (i)   The kilogram is most suitable, but some people still use stones and pounds.
  (ii) The metre would be the most commonly used unit, but you could use yards.
  (iii) The thickness of glass is usually less than 1 cm, so use millimetres.
  (iv) Use centimetres, although some people might use inches.

b Change the following measurements into more sensible units:

  (i)   40 000 mm   (ii) 0.008 kg
  (iii) 136 in   (iv) 0.00 44 m

Solution

  (i)   Change the millimetres to metres by dividing by 1000: $40\,000 \div 1000 = 40$ m
  (ii) Change kilograms to grams by multiplying by 1000: $0.008 \times 1000 = 8$ g
  (iii) Since 12 in = 1 ft, first divide 136 by 12. This gives 11 remainder 4. You now have 11 ft 4 in. You could also change this to 3 yds 2 ft 4 in.
  (iv) Change metres to millimetres by multiplying by 1000: $0.0044 \times 1000 = 4.4$ mm

'Measure something from the zero if possible – because it is the most convenient way!'

c Tim had been asked to measure the length of a key. He hadn't put the ruler in a very sensible position as you can see. How long is the key?

Solution
Using a straight edge, you should check that one end of the key is at 2.3 cm, while the other end of the key is at 4.4 cm. Hence the length of the key is

$$4.4 - 2.3\,\text{cm} = 2.1\,\text{cm}$$

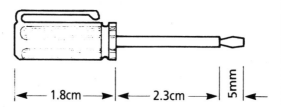

2 a The diagram shows a small pocket screwdriver. What is the total length of the screwdriver?

Solution
The tip of the screwdriver needs to be measured in centimetres. The total length is

$$1.8 + 2.3 + 0.5 = 4.6\,\text{cm}$$

'Change all units to the same one'

b A tube of fruit pastilles is 8.4 cm long. Each sweet is 7 mm thick. How many sweets fit into the tube?

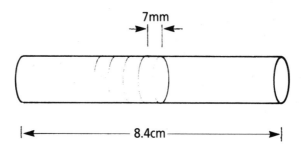

Solution
You must first convert 8.4 cm into 84 mm. The number of sweets is

$$84 \div 7 = 12.$$

Alternatively, you could convert 7 mm into 0.7 cm. The number of sweets is

$$8.4 \div 0.7 = 12.$$

3 **a** A bus service runs every 8 minutes. The first bus in the morning is at 09.00 hours. How many buses are there between 10.00 and 11.00 hours inclusive?

Solution

Timetables are not easy to read, and should always be tackled systematically. Listing the times from 09.00 every 8 minutes, you get:

09.00, 09.08, 09.16, 09.24, 09.32, 09.40, 09.48, 09.56,
10.04, 10.12, 10.20, 10.28, 10.36, 10.44, 10.52, 11.00

By counting, you can see there are eight buses between 10.00 and 11.00.

b The timetable of a local train service is shown alongside.
   (i) How long does the journey take from Haywood to Fultham?
   (ii) If the service runs every 20 minutes, what would be the latest train you could catch at Clapton, to arrive at Sheppy by 12.00 hours?

Haywood	09.35
Clapton	09.52
Ayton	10.06
Sheppy	10.23
Fultham	10.32

Solution

(i) The time taken is

$$\overset{9\ 9\ 2}{10.32} - 9.35 = 57 \text{ minutes}$$

Alternatively,   9.35 to 10.00 is 25 minutes
10.00 to 10.32 is 32 minutes

Total   57 minutes

(ii) Since the service is every 20 minutes, the next few times for arrival at Sheppy are

10.43, 11.03, 11.23, 11.43, 12.03.

So you would have to catch the train that arrived at 11.43. This is the fourth train after the one listed.
   The times from Clapton are 10.12, 10.32, 10.52, 11.12. Therefore you would catch the 11.12.

Do It Yourself

1 a Which units would you use to measure the following:

(i) the volume of an egg;
(ii) the length of a pencil;
(iii) the weight of a lorry;
(iv) the height of a house;
(v) the length of a reel of cotton.

b Change the following measures into more sensible ones:

(i) 800 mm   (ii) 0.06 43 kg   (iii) 900 ft
(iv) 0.28 cm   (v) 84 000 m   (vi) 8600 g

2 a In a local DIY shop, planks of wood 8 mm thick were piled up in a container which is 1 m 20 cm deep. How many layers of wood can be stacked?

b A bookshelf is 1.5 m long. A set of 12 books each of which is 4.3 cm thick is put on to the shelf. How much space is left?

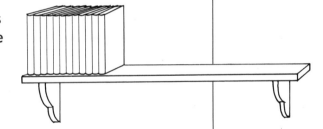

3 a A bus service runs every 12 minutes. There is a bus at 08.10 hours. How many buses are there between 09.00 and 10.00 hours?

b Tim wants to catch a train that leaves at 15.42. It takes 40 minutes to walk to the station, and he needs to allow himself 5 minutes to buy a ticket. What time does he need to set out from home to catch the train?

c Part of a bus timetable is given below:

The service runs every 8 minutes. Jack has arranged to meet Said at the football ground at 11.30. What is the latest bus he can catch from the town centre?

Town centre	09.45
Park	09.56
Post office	10.07
Football ground	10.23

7 Statistics

Things You Need to Know

1 How to record data in the form of a **tally table**. How to choose suitable group sizes to make data easier to read.

2 How to present data in the form of a **bar chart** or **pie chart**, and also how to interpret them.

3 How to use the **mean** (average) and **range** (greatest value–least value) to compare data.

How to Do It

1 A group of friends were testing their response times while playing a driving game. The results in hundredths of a second are as follows:

> 24, 30, 46, 50, 41, 38, 51, 55, 33, 42,
> 50, 47, 38, 29, 38, 50, 46, 42, 35, 47

Put these data into a table choosing suitable size groups.

Solution
First look at the highest and lowest values, which are 24 and 55. Possible groups would be 20–29, 30–39, 40–49, 50–59. You can now complete a tally chart for the data as shown here:

Group	Tally	Frequency
20–29	II	2
30–39	IIII I	6
40–49	IIII II	7
50–59	IIII	5
		Total 20

2a Using the information in question 1, draw (i) a bar chart and (ii) a pie chart to represent the data.

'Choose the group size so that you have four or five groups.'

Solution

(i)

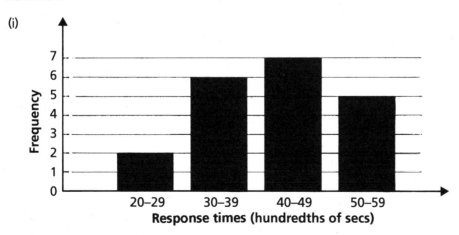

Notice that the bars do not have to touch each other.

'This method is the easiest if the total divides into 360 exactly'

(ii) In order to draw the pie chart, first divide 360° by the total frequency 20. So

$$360 \div 20 = 18°$$

To get the angles of each sector, multiply each frequency by 18°:

Group	Angle
20–29	$2 \times 18 = 36°$
30–39	$6 \times 18 = 108°$
40–49	$7 \times 18 = 126°$
50–59	$5 \times 18 = 90°$

The pie chart can now be drawn.

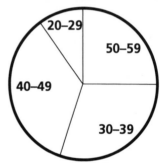

Response times
(hundredths of secs)

b The pie chart shown alongside gives the types of sweets liked most by 30 pupils in Tariq's class. How many of them liked toffees?

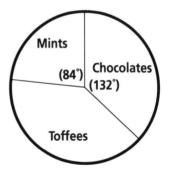

'Simplify the fractions if possible'

Solution

The angle for the toffee sector is

$$360° - 132° - 84° = 144°$$

The fraction that liked toffees

$$= \frac{144}{360} = \frac{2}{5}$$

The number who liked toffees

$$= \frac{2}{5} \times 30 = \frac{60}{5}$$

$$= 12 \text{ pupils}$$

3a There are two different buses Ali can catch to get to work. The waiting times over five days for these two buses are as follows:

Bus A (minutes)   12, 10, 7, 11, 10
Bus B (minutes)   18, 3, 4, 17, 3

Which bus would you recommend Ali catches? Give reasons for your answer.

Solution
The average waiting time for each bus is

A $(12+10+7+11+10) \div 5 = 10$ minutes
B $(18+ 3+4+17+ 3) \div 5 = 9$ minutes

The range (largest − smallest) for each bus is

A $12-7 = 5$ minutes
B $18-3 = 15$ minutes

If you only had the average times, you would recommend bus B, but the range of times for this bus is much greater than for A. Hence the mean and range together suggest that Ali should catch bus A.

b The average weight of five boys is 50 kg, and the average weight of four girls is 44 kg. What is the average weight of all nine children?

Solution
Be careful – the answer is not $(50+44) \div 2$
The total weight of the boys $= 5 \times 50$ $= 250$ kg
The total weight of the girls $= 4 \times 44$ $= 176$ kg
The total weight of the children $= 250+176 = 426$ kg
Hence the average weight $= 426 \div 9$ $= 47.3$ kg.

'To find the average, or mean, of a set of numbers, add them together then divide by how many numbers there are in the set'

'To know the range of a set of numbers, subtract the smallest number from the largest number'

Do It Yourself

1 Every morning for nearly 3 weeks, Jane went into the garden to collect snails. The numbers that she found are given in the following table:

Mon.	Tues.	Wed.	Thur.	Fri.	Sat.	Sun.
4	8	15	20	6	12	9
23	14	8	4	20	2	16
25	16	10	3	5	18	

She decided to record these results in a table with groups 1–5, 6–10, 11–15, etc. Complete the tally chart Jane got.

2 a The diagram shows the number of cars of different colours recorded by Jodi outside his house in 1 hour on Saturday morning.

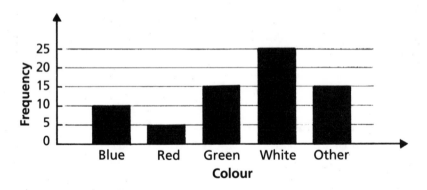

(i) How many cars did he count altogether?

(ii) How many more green cars did he see than red ones?

b Use your answers from question 1 to draw a pie chart and a bar chart to represent Jane's data.

c Janice interviewed 60 people about which sport they liked most. She put the results into a pie chart as shown. How many people liked each of the four sports?

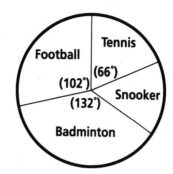

3a Two types of batteries (A and B) were tried in a small toy. The times (minutes) that they lasted are given in the following table:

A	40	36	50	41	63
B	50	32	51	46	51

By calculating the means and ranges of these times, suggest which battery is the best type to use.

b The average weight of six parcels is 2 kg. The average weight of another four parcels is 3 kg. What is the average weight of all ten parcels?

c The average cost of four rail tickets was £6. The average cost of eight different tickets was £4. What is the average cost of all 12 tickets?

8

Probability

Things You Need to Know

1 Probability measures the chance of something happening (how likely it is). There is a scale of probabilities going from 0 (impossible) to 1 (certain).

The sun will disappear tomorrow

A ball will fall to the ground if dropped

0   1

Between 0 and 1, a probability is written as a fraction or decimal.

2 Probabilities are calculated from (i) theory (using equally likely outcomes); (ii) experiments; (iii) surveys; (iv) looking back over previous records.

$$\text{Probability} = \frac{\text{number of favourable outcomes}}{\text{total number of outcomes}}$$

How to Do It

1 On the probability scale below, mark approximately the position of the following events happening:
  (i) a coin landing heads when spun;
  (ii) a die scoring six if rolled;
  (iii) two pupils in your class having the same birthday;
  (iv) Manchester United winning the Premiership title;
  (v) you doing well in your maths test.

Solution

  (i) There are equal chances of heads or tails, so the probability is about 0.5.
  (ii) About one-sixth of the way along.
  (iii) There is actually quite a reasonable chance of this happening, perhaps not much less than (ii).
  (iv) It is quite small—though supporters might well think otherwise!
  (v) Let's hope this is nearly certain.

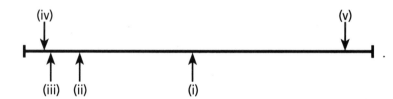

> *'Answers to this sort of question can only be estimated'*

2ᵃ There are different ways of estimating probabilities. For example:

Method A: using equally likely outcomes. If I wanted to know the probability of rolling a six with a die, the answer is $\frac{1}{6}$ because there are six equally likely outcomes.

Method B: looking back over records or data. If I wanted to know the probability that a hurricane would happen in South America this week, I would look back at old weather records.

Method C: carrying out a survey or experiment. If I wanted to estimate the number of the next bus to arrive at a bus stop, I would do a survey of the buses arriving at that bus stop.

'This is a popular type of question'

For the following situations, say whether you would use method A, B or C:
  (i)   The probability that a pupil in your class likes chocolate.
  (ii) The probability that you will win a prize in a draw if you buy 5 tickets, and 1000 are sold.
  (iii) The probability that it will snow in London on 25th December.
  (iv) The probability that an egg will break if you drop it into a saucepan of water.
  (v)   The probability that an accident occurs on a particular road next week.

Solution

  (i)   Method C: survey the class.
  (ii) Method A: $\frac{5}{1000}$
  (iii) Method B: look at old weather records.
  (iv) Method C: carry out an experiment.
  (v)   Method B: you would look at police accident records for that road over a period of many weeks.

b Lucy plays for her school's hockey team. In the last eight games, the goals scored by various people in the team are shown in the table below:

'Make sure you understand what the table says'

Name	Lucy	Pam	Vikki	Rachel	Jacinta
Goals scored	2	4	1	5	3

In the next game, what is the probability that Pam scores the first goal?

Solution
This is an example of calculating probabilities from looking at past data.
  The total number of goals is

$$2+4+1+5+3 = 15$$

Of these, Pam scored 4. So the probability that Pam scores the next goal is $\frac{4}{15}$.

c If two coins are spun into the air and land on the floor, what is the probability that they both land heads?

Solution

This requires listing the equally likely outcomes as follows:

| Coin | Coin | Coin | Coin | Coin | Coin | Coin | Coin |
| 1 | 2 | 1 | 2 | 1 | 2 | 1 | 2 |

'Note that TH and HT are different outcomes'

You can see there are *four* outcomes, one of which is both heads. The probability of both heads $= \frac{1}{4}$.

Note: The answer $\frac{1}{3}$ is wrong because the outcomes 'obtaining two heads' and 'obtaining one head and one tail' are *not* **equally likely**.

Do It Yourself

1 Draw a line to represent the probability scale, and mark approximately the point where the following probabilities would occur:

    (i) scoring an even number with a simple roll of a die;

    (ii) a sunny day if the previous day was sunny;

    (iii) a hockey match ending with a score 0–0;

    (iv) drawing a spade from a complete pack of playing cards;

    (v) a Premiership side winning the FA Cup;

    (vi) passing a driving test first time;

    (vii) a coin landing heads;

    (viii) a professional darts player hitting a double that he is aiming for.

2a Using the definitions of methods A, B and C used earlier in this unit, state which method you would use to calculate the following probabilities:

    (i) drawing an ace from a pack of cards;

    (ii) rolling a score of six with a loaded (biased) die;

    (iii) rain on the first Saturday in August;

    (iv) that the next person that goes into a supermarket will buy a bottle of 'SUDSO' washing-up liquid;

    (v) that the Labour Party will win the next by-election in your area.

b If three coins are spun into the air and land on a table without rolling off, draw up a list of all of the equally likely outcomes. What is the probability that two of the coins show heads?

c Aneka carried out a survey of favourite flavoured crisps in her class. The results are as follows:

Type	Plain	Salt and vinegar	Beef	Chicken	Spring onion
Number	5	2	4	6	3

What is the probability that somebody chosen at random from the class likes chicken?

d Two dice are rolled and the score is obtained by adding the number of spots showing. Draw a table to show the 36 ways in which the two dice can land. Find the probability that:

   (i) the score is 7;
  (ii) the score is less than 4;
 (iii) the score is not 12.

Angles and Triangles

9

Things You Need to Know

1 Angles:
   (i) There are 360 degrees (°) in a complete turn.
   (ii) Angles less than 90° are called **acute**.
   (iii) Angles between 90° and 180° are called **obtuse**.
   (iv) Angles greater than 180° are called **reflex**.
   (v) An angle of 90° is called a **right angle**: symbol ∟.
       Lines at right angles are **perpendicular**.
   (vi) Angles on a straight line add up
        to 180°.

   $a+b = 180°$

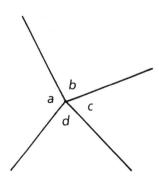

   (vii) Angles at a point add up to 360°

   $a+b+c+d = 360°$

   (viii) The angles of a triangle add up to 180°.

2 Parallel lines (marked with arrows)

$a = b$: **opposite angles**

$\left.\begin{array}{l} a = c \\ d = e \end{array}\right\}$ **alternate angles** (sometimes called 'z' angles)

$c = b$: **corresponding angles** (sometimes called 'F' angles)

$\left.\begin{array}{l} d + c = 180° \\ a + e = 180° \end{array}\right\}$ **interior angles**

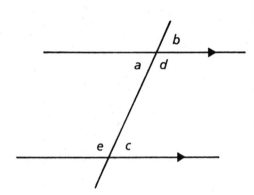

3 How to construct a triangle accurately using a ruler, pair of compasses and a protractor. (Make sure you have a sharp pencil, and that you can clearly read the measurements on the ruler and protractor.)

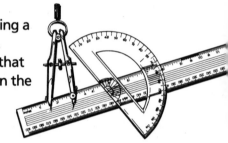

How to Do It

1 Calculate the value of x in the following diagrams:

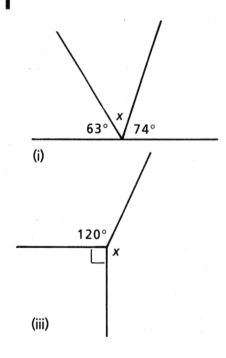

(i)

(iii)

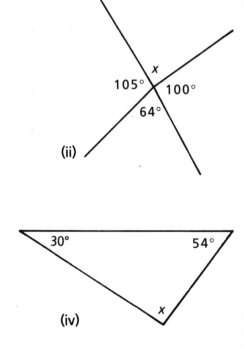

(ii)

(iv)

Solution

(i) Angles on a straight line add up to 180°. Hence

$$x + 63° + 74° = 180°$$
$$x = 180° - 63° - 74° = 43°$$

(ii) Angles at a point add up to 360°. So

$$x + 100° + 105° + 64° = 360°$$
$$x = 360° - 100° - 105° - 64° = 91°$$

(iii) Remember ∟ means 90°. So

$$120° + 90° + x = 360°$$
$$x = 360° - 120° - 90° = 150°$$

(iv) The angles of a triangle add up to 180°. Hence

$$30° + 54° + x = 180°$$
$$x = 180° - 30° - 54° = 96°$$

2 In the diagram calculate the values of angles *a*, *b* and *c*.

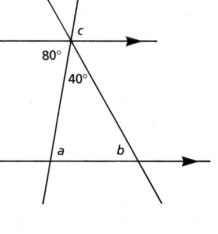

'Give clear reasons for your answers'

Solution

$a = 80°$
(alternate angles)

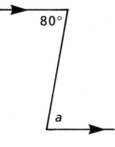

$b = 180° - 80° - 40°$
$= 60°$
(angles of a triangle)

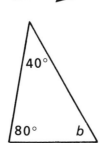

$c = 80°$ (corresponding angles)

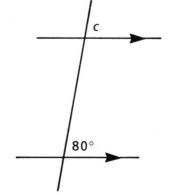

57

3

a Construct the triangle ABC with angle A = 20°, angle C = 80° and AB = 6.4 cm. Measure AC. A sketch is shown alongside.

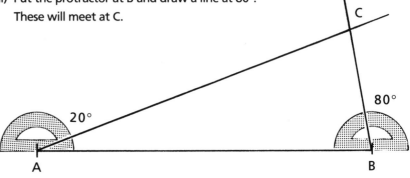

Solution

(i) Draw the base line AB first.
(ii) Put the protractor at A, and draw a line at 20°.
(iii) Put the protractor at B and draw a line at 80°. These will meet at C.

'Make sure you read the correct scale from 0° on the protractor'

Measure AC = 6.4 cm.

b Three sticks of length 4 cm, 5.6 cm and 3.8 cm are joined together to make a triangle. Make an accurate drawing of the triangle, and measure the three angles.

Solution

You will need a pair of compasses for this question.

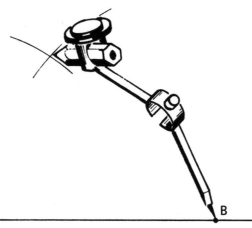

(i) Draw a base line 5.6 cm long.
(ii) Open the compasses to 4 cm, put the point on one end (A) and draw an arc.
(iii) Open the compasses to 3.8 cm, and put the point on the other end (B). Draw another arc making sure that the two arcs meet.
(iv) The point where the two arcs meet is the other point of the triangle.

(v) The triangle can now be completed.

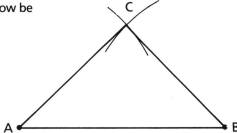

(vi) Measuring gives:

A = 43°   B = 46°   C = 91°

Do It Yourself

1 a (i) For the following angles, state whether they are acute, obtuse or reflex:

(a) 80°   (b) 200°   (c) 95°   (d) 400°   (e) 175°

(ii) How many complete turns are there in:

(a) 720°   (b) 3600°

(iii) How many quarter-turns are there in:

(a) 270°   (b) 450°   (c) 630°

b Find angle *x* in the following diagrams:

(i)

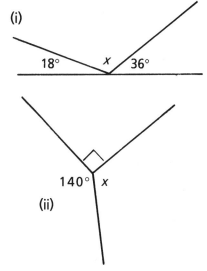

(ii)

(iii)

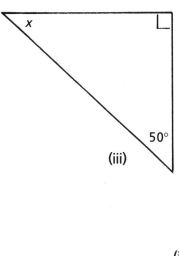

(iv)

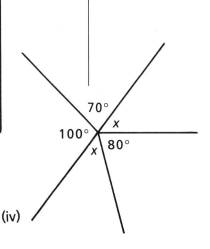

2 Find the values of the letters in the following diagrams. Give a reason where possible.

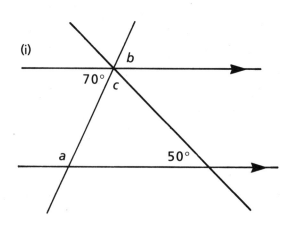

(i)

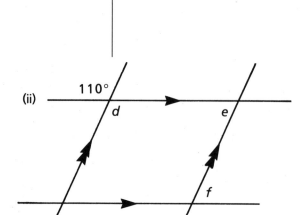

(ii)

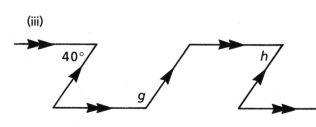

(iii)

3 a The diagram shows part of a net for making a triangular prism. Make an accurate drawing of face A, and measure the three angles.

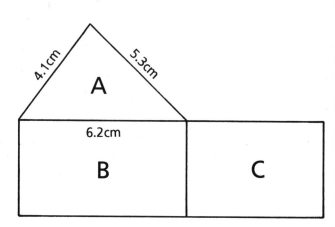

b Construct accurately the following triangles:

    (i) PQR, where PQ = 8 cm, angle P = 25°, angle Q = 48°.
        Measure the length PR.

    (ii) ABC, where AB = 6 cm, BC = 4.6 cm, AC = 5.8 cm.
        Measure angle A.

Coordinates and Scale Drawing

Things You Need to Know

1 How to locate the position of a point using **cartesian coordinates** (*x*, *y*).
(You can think of coordinates as the address of a point.)

The coordinates are located by means of labelled axes, which meet at an origin 0. The *x*–axis is horizontal and the *y*–axis is vertical.

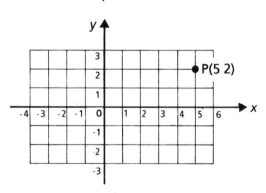

2 When making a drawing of something, it is often not done full size, but to scale (on a map for example). So a scale of 1 : 80 or $\frac{1}{80}$ means that 1 cm on the drawing represents 80 cm on the real object.

How to Do It

1 a Plot the following points on a grid: A(−3, −2), B(−1, 2), C(3, 2) and D(5, −2). What name do we give to the shape ABCD?

Solution

The shape is plotted as shown in the diagram. Be careful with the negative signs.

You can see that BC and AD are parallel but AB and DC are not, hence ABCD is a **trapezium**.

"Make sure you get x and y the right way round"

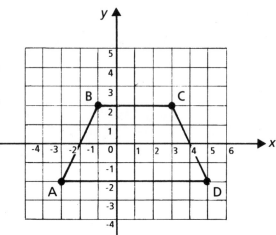

b The shape PQRST has a line of symmetry. If P is (−3, 2), Q(0, 6), R(3, 2) and T(−2, −2), what could the coordinates of point S be?

Solution

First plot the points that have been given as shown. Although you do not know the position of S, if you look carefully the y−axis can be the line of symmetry. (Is it the only one?)

Hence S must be (2, −2).

"You may need tracing paper"

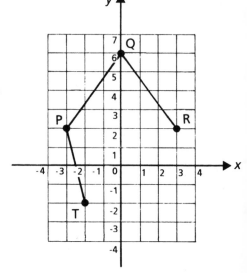

2 a The sketch shows the plan of the ground floor of a house. Make a scale drawing of this using a scale of 1:50.

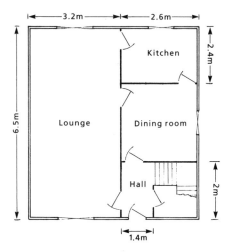

Solution

A scale of 1:50 means 1 cm represents 50 cm. Hence 2 cm represents 100 cm = 1 m. So, for example,

4.2 m is represented by $4.2 \times 2 = 8.4$ cm

The scale drawing is shown below.

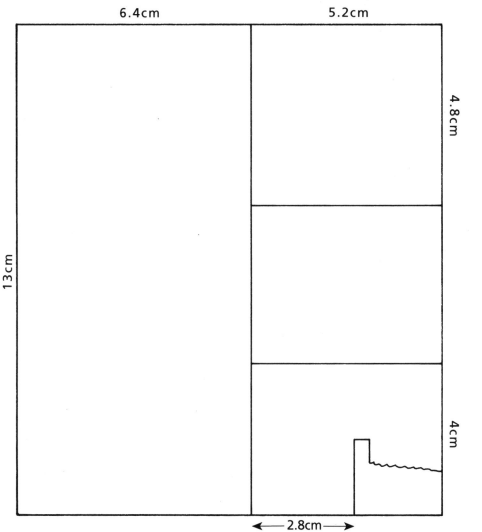

'A scale shows how many times bigger one quantity is than another'

b A map is drawn to a scale of 1 : 50 000. Find:
  (i) the distance between two points on the map that are 4.8 km apart;
  (ii) the length of a railway tunnel that is 3.6 cm long on the map.

Solution

Method 1

    1 : 50 000 means 1 cm = 50 000 cm.
  (i) Now 4.8 km = 4800 m = 480 000 cm.

      480 000 ÷ 50 000 = 9.6

    Hence the distance = 9.6 cm.
  (ii) 3.6 cm represents

      3.6 × 50 000 cm = 180 000 cm
                  = 1800 m (Divide by 100 because 100 cm = 1 m)
                  = 1.8 km (Divide by 1000 because 1000 m = 1 km)

    Hence the tunnel is 1.8 km long.

'Method 2 is definitely easier to use, especially in more difficult work'

Method 2
50 000 cm = 0.5 km, and so the map scale would be written:

  1 cm represents 0.5 km or 2 cm represents 1 km

  (i) 4.8 km is represented by 2 × 4.8 = 9.6 cm;
  (ii) 3.6 cm represents 3.6 × 0.5 = 1.8 km.

Do It Yourself

1 a Plot the following shapes on a square grid labelled from −10 to +10 on both the *x*– and *y*–axes. In each case, name the shape formed.

    (i) A(−1, 4), B(5, 4), C(5, −2), D(−1, −2)
    (ii) P(0, 10), Q(5, 0), R(−5, 0)
    (iii) E(−5, 1), F(8, 1), G(4, −4), H(−1, −4)
    (iv) J(0, 10), K(10, 0), L(0, −10), M(−10, 0)
    (v) R(0, −2), S(−2, 0), T(4, 6), U(6, 4)

b The points $(-3, 3)$ and $(4, -3)$ are two corners of a rectangle, and the line joining these points is the diagonal of the rectangle. Draw this information on a grid and join up two different rectangles that satisfy these conditions.

c Plot the points P(2, 2), Q(4, 5) and R(-4, 5). What are the coordinates of S if PQRS is a parallelogram?

2a The diagram shown alongside is a sketch of the side of a shed. The window is centred between the door and the end, and the bottom of the window is 80 cm above ground level. Make an accurate drawing of the side view using a scale of 1:20.

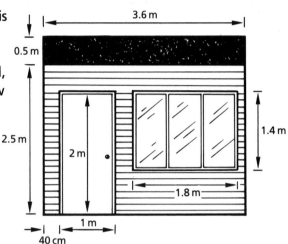

b A map has been drawn using a scale of 1:25 000. Find:

    (i) the distance on the map between two villages that are 15 km apart;

    (ii) the measurements of a cultivated forest that is 3 cm by 4.6 cm on the map.

c The diagram shown here has been drawn to a scale of 1:50. What lengths in metres are represented by a, b and c?

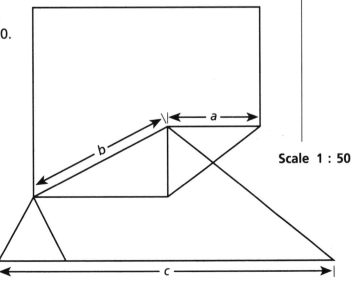

Scale 1 : 50

11 | Area and Volume

Things You Need to Know

1 The **area** of a shape is the measure of how much it covers. You can always find an area by laying a square grid over a shape and counting the squares—but there are often easier methods of calculating the area.

Area is measured in square millimetres (mm²), square centimetres (cm²), square metres (m²) and so on. Choose the unit depending on how large the shape is.

You may need to use one of the formulae given here to find the area.

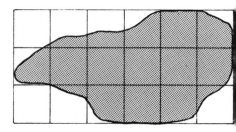

Square   Area = a²   Rectangle   Area = ab

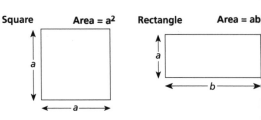

Triangle   Area = ¹/₂ base × height

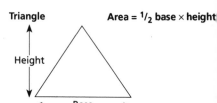

2 Volume measures how much space a shape fills. Volume can be measured from units of cubic centimetres (cm³) or mm³ or m³, etc., in a similar way to area.

You may need to use a formula to find a volume as shown alongside.

Cuboid

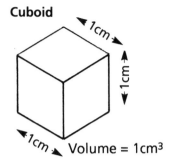

Volume = 1cm³

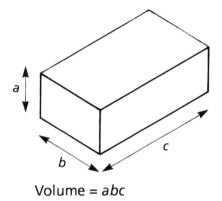

Volume = abc

Triangular prism

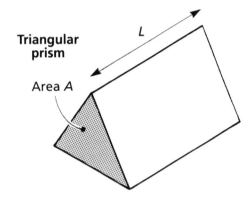

Area A

Volume = area of triangle x length
= $A L$

How to Do It

1 a The diagram shows the plan of a kitchen. It is to be fitted with floor tiles which measure 0.5 m × 0.5 m.
   (i) How many tiles will be needed?
   (ii) What is the area of the kitchen?

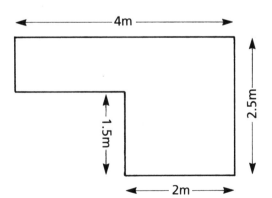

'Check how many times 0.5 m divides into each length'

Solution

The best way to solve this problem is to draw how the tiles will fit. It needn't be completely accurate as long as you make sure they fit. The diagram alongside shows this.

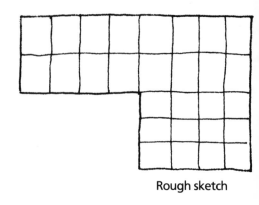

Rough sketch

(i) Counting the tiles, you get 28.

(ii) The area of each tile is

$$0.5 \times 0.5 = 0.25 \, \text{m}^2$$

The area of the floor is

$$28 \times 0.25 = 7 \, \text{m}^2$$

b The perimeter of a square is 8.4 cm. What is its area?

Solution

A square has four equal sides, hence the length of one side is

$$8.4 \div 4 = 4.1 \, \text{cm}.$$

The area of the square is

$$4.1 \times 4.1 = 16.81 \, \text{cm}^2$$

You could use the square button on your calculator. So

Display

$$\boxed{4.1} \rightarrow \boxed{x^2} \rightarrow \boxed{16.81}$$

c If the area of a square is 49 cm², what is the perimeter?

Solution

To find the side of a square given the area, you have to do the reverse of squaring. This is, of course, square rooting.

Now 49 is a perfect square, hence

$$\sqrt{49} = 7$$

The side of the square = 7 cm. The perimeter of the square is

$$4 \times 7 = 28 \, \text{cm}.$$

You could of course use the  button on your calculator. So

Display

49 ⇨ √ ⇨ 7.0

'*Read your calculator instruction booklet*'

d The diagram shows an old-fashioned road sign. What is the area of this sign?

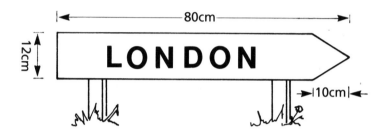

Solution

Split the area into two parts as follows:

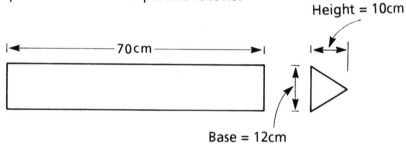

The area of the rectangle is

$$12 \times 70 = 840 \text{ cm}^2$$

The area of the triangle is

$$\tfrac{1}{2} \times 12 \times 10 = 60 \text{ cm}^2$$

The area of the sign is

$$840 + 60 = 900 \text{ cm}^2$$

2 **a** Orange juice is sold in containers which measure 8 cm by 12 cm by 6 cm. The juice is poured into glasses that hold 36 ml. How many glasses can you fill?

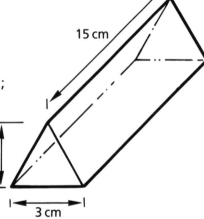

Remember
$1\,cm^3 = 1\,ml$

Solution
The volume of the carton is

$$8 \times 12 \times 6 = 576\,cm^3 = 576\,ml$$

Since each glass holds 36 ml, the number of glasses is

$$576 \div 36 = 16$$

b Chocolate is sold in containers in the shape of a triangular prism. The measurements of the prism are shown in the diagram.
Calculate
(i) the area of the triangular cross section;
(ii) the volume of the chocolate bar.

This shape is a prism

15 cm

3 cm

3 cm

Solution
(i) The area of a triangle $= \frac{1}{2}$(base $\times$ height) and so is

$$\tfrac{1}{2}(3 \times 3) = \tfrac{1}{2} \times 9 = 4.5\,cm^2$$

(ii) The volume of the bar $=$ area of the triangle $\times$ length and so is

$$4.5 \times 15 = 67.5\,cm^3$$

c An engineering component is in the shape of a block measuring 3 cm by 1.5 cm by 2 cm. A hole of 1 cm square cross-section goes through the centre as shown. What volume of metal is needed to make the component?

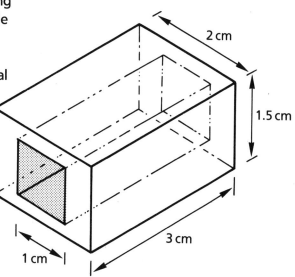

Solution

If the block did not have a hole in it, the volume would be

$1.5 \times 3 \times 2 = 9 \, cm^3$

The volume of the hole is

$1 \times 1 \times 3 = 3 \, cm^3$

Hence the volume of the component is

$9 - 3 = 6 \, cm^3$

'Always subtract the volume of the hole from the total'

Do It Yourself

1 a The area of a square is 25 cm². What is the perimeter of the square?

b A large table is made from six equal triangular shapes as shown in the diagram. Find:
 (i) the area of one triangle;
 (ii) the area of the table.

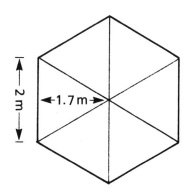

c Find the area of the shape shown alongside.

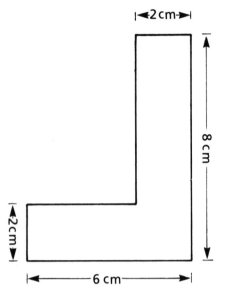

2a This solid block has height 6 cm and width 4 cm. If the volume of the block is 192 cm³, what is the length of the block?

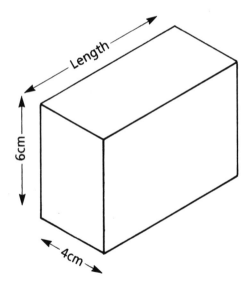

b A wooden trunk measures inside 50 cm by 60 cm by 40 cm deep. It is filled with coloured bricks each of which is a cube of side 10 cm. How many bricks could you pack into the trunk?

c Holly was given a tent for Christmas. The dimensions of the tent are shown in the diagram. Find:

(i) the volume of the tent in cubic metres;

(ii) the volume of the tent in cubic centimetres.

How do you convert cubic metres into cubic centimetres?

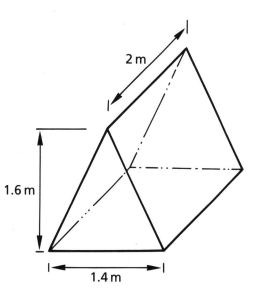

d Part of an engine mounting is in the shape of a block measuring 15 cm by 12 cm by 10 cm. A cube of side 4 cm is removed from one corner as shown. What is the volume of the mounting?

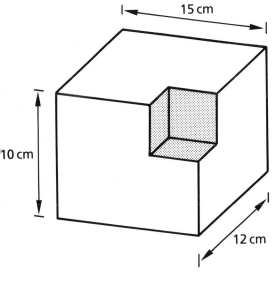

73

12 | Symmetry and Congruent Shapes

Things You Need to Know

1 **Line symmetry** is where a two-dimensional shape is exactly the same either side of a **mirror line**, or **line of symmetry**.

2 A solid can have a **plane of symmetry** if it is exactly the same on either side of a plane. In the diagram below, the shape also has another plane of symmetry, shown −−−−−.

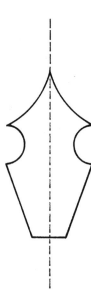

Mirror line

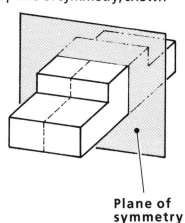

Plane of symmetry

3 Two shapes that are exactly the same are said to be **congruent**.

4 A shape has **rotational symmetry** if it can be rotated about a point (the **centre of rotation**) until it coincides with itself. The number of times this happens between 0 and 360° is called the **order of rotation**.

Order of rotational symmetry = 4

How to Do It

1 Draw a reasonable sketch to show all the lines of symmetry on the following shapes:
  (i) a rectangle;
  (ii) a regular hexagon;
  (iii) a kite.

'Mirror lines are usually shown as dotted lines like this'

Solution

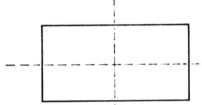

  (i) A rectangle has two lines of symmetry.

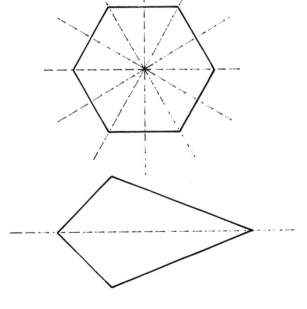

  (ii) A hexagon has six lines of symmetry.

  (iii) A kite has only one line of symmetry.

2 How many planes of symmetry does a cube have?

'This is a difficult problem. Make yourself a cube and try it'

Solution

Imagine four cuts through the top (or bottom) of the cube (shown dotted). Each will give a plane of symmetry.

Through one side face there are three more cuts different from the first set.

We now have seven planes of symmetry. Finally, looking from the front, there are two more that we don't have already. Hence the number of planes of symmetry is

$$4+3+2 = 9.$$

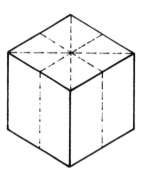 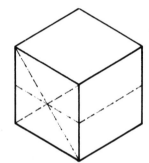 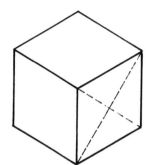

3 ABCD is a rectangle. Name three pairs of congruent triangles in the figure.

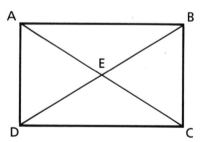

Solution

Remember congruent means exactly the same even if you have to rotate the shape, or flip it over. Here are three possible pairs.

ABE and DCE
AED and BEC
ABC and ADC

Can you find any more?

4 **a** On the grid shown alongside, shade three other squares so that the shape has rotational symmetry of order 4.

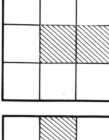

Solution

Taking the centre of the square as the centre of rotation, the square on the right must repeat itself every 90°. The resulting shape is shown alongside.

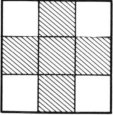

b Mark with a cross the centre of rotation for the pattern shown below.

'Tracing paper is useful here'

Solution

(i) Join any two pairs of corresponding points, say A_1A_2 and B_1B_2.

(ii) Draw line L_1 through the centre of A_1A_2 at right angles to it.

(iii) Draw line L_2 through the centre of B_1B_2 at right angles to it.

(iv) Lines L_1 and L_2 meet at the centre of rotation.

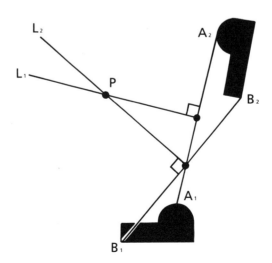

'This construction must be accurate. Check your answer with tracing paper'

Do It Yourself

1 **a** Draw all the lines of symmetry on the following shapes:

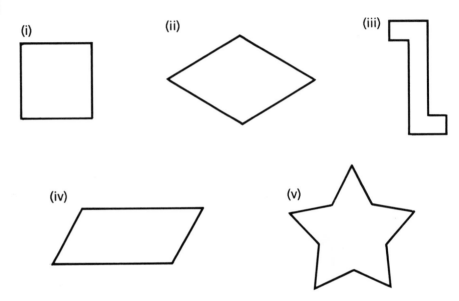

(i)　　　　　　　(ii)　　　　　　　(iii)

(iv)　　　　　　　(v)

b Which of the following letters of the alphabet only have *lines* of symmetry?

A D H L M S T V W

2 **a** How many planes of symmetry does a cuboid have?

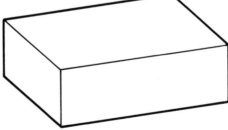

b Give a sketch of a solid that has two planes of symmetry.

3 The diagram shows a grid with 10 triangles drawn on it. Arrange the triangles into groups which are congruent to each other.

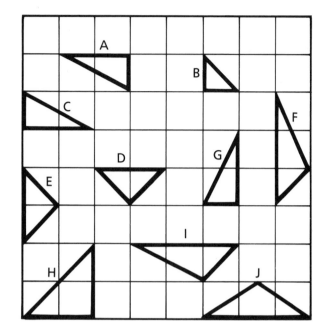

4 For the shapes below, indicate where the centre of rotational symmetry is, and state the order of rotational symmetry.

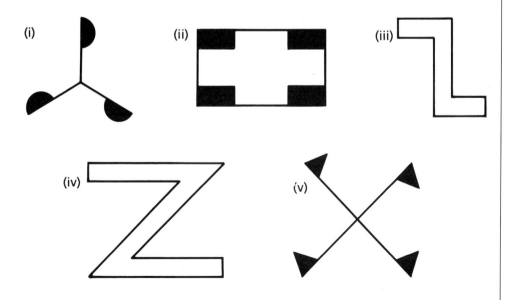

(i)

(ii)

(iii)

(iv)

(v)

13 | Algebra

Things You Need to Know

1 When using letters in algebra, remember that the letters represent numbers. Note:

ab means $a \times b$

$\dfrac{a}{b}$ means $a \div b$

An **expression** is any statement containing letters,
e.g. $4N = 3$, $at + y$, x^2.

An expression is **evaluated** if the letters are replaced by numbers.

An expression can be used to represent a **rule** given in a **number machine**.

2 There are certain rules that you need to know when working with algebra:

(i) $a \times b = b \times a = ab = ba$

(ii) $a + a = 2a$

(iii) $x \times x = x^2$

(iv) $a \div 4 = \frac{1}{4}a$

(v) $a \times 0 = 0 \times a = 0$

(vi) $a(b + c)$ means add b and c first and then multiply the answer by a.

How to Do It

1 a Write down an expression to go with the following:
   (i) Multiplying a number N by 6 and subtracting 3 from the answer.
   (ii) The cost of p oranges at t pence each.
   (iii) The average score by a batsman who scored x, y and z runs in three different matches.
   (iv) The number of people on a bus if it arrives with A people, x get off and y get on.

Solution

(i) $N \times 6$ is better written $6 \times N$ or $6N$. The final expression is

$$6N - 3$$

(ii) To find the total cost you simply multiply the number of oranges by the cost of each one. Hence the expression is

$$p \times t \quad \text{or} \quad pt$$

(iii) To find an average score, you add the scores and divide by the number of times the person batted, in this case three. The average is

$$(x+y+z) \div 3 \quad \text{or} \quad \frac{x+y+z}{3} \quad \text{or} \quad \tfrac{1}{3}(x+y+z)$$

(iv) You have to subtract x, and then add y. The number on the bus is

$$A - x + y.$$

b Evaluate the following expressions:
   (i) $4x + 2y$ if $x = 3$ and $y = 5$
   (ii) Ht^2 if $H = 4$ and $t = 3$
   (iii) $\dfrac{x}{y+z}$ if $x = 25$, $y = 2$ and $x = 3$

Solution

(i) $4 \times 3 + 2 \times 5 = 12 + 10 = 22$
(ii) $4 \times 3^2 = 4 \times 9 = 36$
(iii) $\dfrac{25}{2+3} = \dfrac{25}{5} = 5$

c The area of a trapezium is given by the formula

$$\text{Area} = \frac{(a+b)h}{2}$$

Use this formula to find the area of the trapezium given alongside.

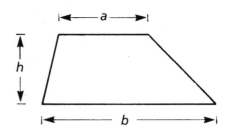

Solution

Here $a = 5.8$, $b = 7.9$, $h = 3.1$. Substitute into the formula:

$$\text{Area} = \frac{(5.8+7.9)3.1}{2}$$

$$= \frac{13.7 \times 3.1}{2} = \frac{42.47}{2} = 21.235 \text{ cm}^2$$

A sensible answer would be 21.2 cm² (three significant figures).

d Write down the rule that goes with the following function machines:

(i) In $+3$ Out

    x y

(ii) In $\times 4$ $+6$ Out

    R H

(iii) In $\div 2$ -5 Out

    T Q

Solution

Remember that the letter under 'Out' appears on the left-hand side of the equal sign.

(i) The rule is $y = x+3$.

(ii) The rule is $H = R \times 4 + 6$. This is better if written $H = 4R+6$

(iii) The rule is $Q = T \div 2 - 5$. This is better if written $Q = \frac{1}{2}T - 5$ or $Q = \frac{T}{2} - 5$

2 **a** Find an expression for the perimeter of the shape given alongside.

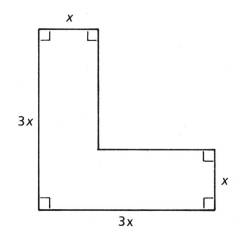

Solution

Some lengths appear to be missed out, but you can work them out. They must both be 2x. The perimeter is

$$x + 2x + 2x + x + 3x + 3x = 12x$$

b Write more simply:

(i) $a \times b \times 2$ (ii) $a \times b + b \times a$

(iii) $2x \times 2x$ (iv) $a \div 4 + b \div 3$

(v) $4a + 3t + 2a + 5t$

Solution

(i) The number should always be written at the front, so

$$a \times b \times 2 = 2 \times a \times b$$

The $\times$ signs can be missed out. Hence

$$a \times b \times 2 = 2ab$$

(ii) $a \times b + b \times a = ab + ba$

But ab and ba are the same, so we have two lots of ab. Hence

$$a \times b + b \times a = 2ab \text{ or } 2ba$$

(iii) $2x \times 2x$ means

$$2 \times x \times 2 \times x = 2 \times 2 \times x \times x$$
$$= 4 \times x^2 = 4x^2$$

(iv) $a \div 4 = \frac{1}{4}a$ and $b \div 3 = \frac{1}{3}b$

Hence $a \div 4 + b \div 3 = \frac{1}{4}a + \frac{1}{3}b$

(v) $4a + 2a = 6a$
$3t + 5t = 8t$

Hence $4a + 3t + 2a + 5t = 6a + 8t$

If you have started to learn how to factorise, this could be written $2(3a + 4t)$.

83

Do It Yourself

1 **a** Write down an expression for the following:

      (i) Doubling a number N and subtracting 5.

      (ii) Taking away 8 from the square of X.

      (iii) The amount taken at a hockey match if N spectators pay £3 each.

      (iv) The average mark scored by Janine in her exams if she scored M marks in maths, B marks in biology and C marks in chemistry.

      (v) The result of adding the square of x to the square of y.

b Work out the following:

      (i) pq^2 if $p = 3$ and $q = 6$

      (ii) $5x - 2y$ if $x = 8$ and $y = 3$

      (iii) $\dfrac{H}{t + T}$ if $t = 3$, $T = 6$ and $H = 18$

      (iv) $a(b + c)$ if $a = 5$, $b = 3$ and $c = 4$

c The circumference C of a circle of radius r can be found from the formula $C = 6.28r$.

      (i) Find the circumference of a circle of radius 12 mm.

      (ii) Find the circumference of a circle of diameter 20 m.

      (iii) Find the radius of a circle of circumference 50 km.

d The area of a circle A of radius r can be found from the formula $A = 3.1r^2$.

      (i) Find the area of a circle of radius 4 cm.

      (ii) Find the radius of a circle of area 100 cm².

e This question is about the following number machine:

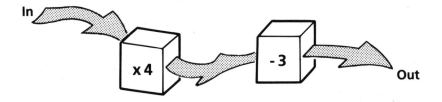

Complete the following table:

In		Out
3	$\longrightarrow$	9
11	$\longrightarrow$	☐
4	$\longrightarrow$	☐
5	$\longrightarrow$	☐
☐	$\longrightarrow$	25

What is the rule that connects In (x) and Out (y)?

2 a Write the following in a simpler way:

(i) $x \times y \times 8$ (ii) $2 \times p \times q + q \times p$

(iii) $3x \times 2x$ (iv) $4H + 6k + 2H + 5k$

(v) $3x \times x - x \times x$ (vi) $6x^2 + 5x - 2x^2 + 3x$

b An octagon has eight sides of length x centimetres. If the perimeter of the octagon is p centimetres, write down a rule that connects p and x. Use your rule to find p if $x = 6.6$ cm.

$\longleftarrow x \longrightarrow$

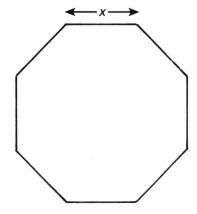

c A fence is made using P posts and R rails. One post costs £6, and one rail costs £2. Write down an expression for the cost C of the posts and rails. Work out the cost of buying 12 posts and 24 rails.

85

14 Decision Trees, Networks and Tables

Things You Need to Know

1 A **decision tree** or **flow chart** is a useful way of writing a set of instructions. They are often used by computer programmers.

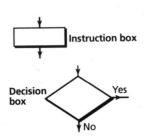

2 A **network** is a number of points joined by lines. They are not drawn to scale but show the relative positions of the points to each other.

3 Information can be stored in a table of rows and columns. This can lead to easy recall of data.

How to Do It

1 The flow chart given below can be used for sorting shapes. Follow it through for:
 (i) a triangle;
 (ii) a square;
 (iii) a parallelogram.

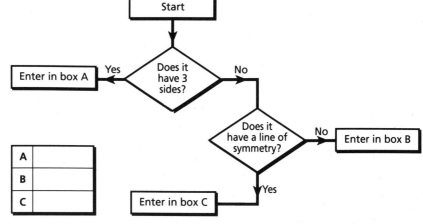

Solution

(i) A triangle has three sides so enter **triangle** in box A.
(ii) A square does not have three sides, but it does have lines of symmetry, so enter **square** in box B.
(iii) A parallelogram does not have three sides, nor does it have lines of symmetry, so enter **parallelogram** in box C. The solution is

A	triangle
B	square
C	parallelogram

'To sort out the shapes, think of things which make them different'

2 The network alongside shows the distances between the houses of four friends, Alex, Brenda, Colin and David. Alex leaves home to drop a message into each house then returns home. What is the shortest journey he can make in total?

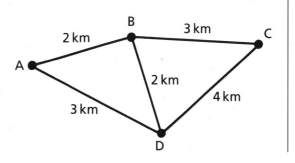

'The network is not drawn to scale'

Solution

There are several routes:

> ABCDA
> ADBCDA   (not sensible)
> ADCBA
> ABDCBA   (not sensible)

There are others which are even longer:

> ABCDA distance $= 2+3+4+3 = 12\,\text{km}$
> ADCBA distance $= 3+4+3+2 = 12\,\text{km}$

Either of these routes will do.

3 The table shows the number of pets owned by Jason, Josie and Rupert.

	Cats	Fish	Birds
Jason	1	4	1
Josie	0	2	2
Rupert	2	0	2

'Each number in a table is called a cell'

  (i) How many pets do they own between them?
 (ii) How many pets does Rupert have?
(iii) Who owns the most pets?

Solution

(i) To get the total number, add up all the numbers in the table:

> $1+4+1+2+2+2+2 = 14$ pets

(ii) Add the number in Rupert's row:

> Total $= 2+0+2 = 4$ pets

(iii) Jason has 6 pets.

Do It Yourself

1 a The decision tree shown here sorts numbers. Work through it with the numbers 1 to 10 inclusive and enter the answers in the appropriate boxes.

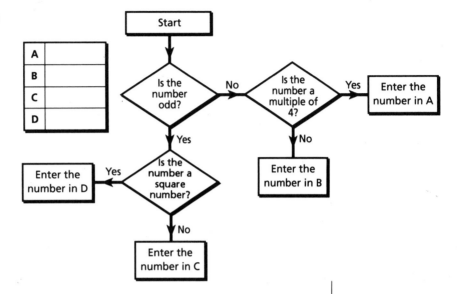

A	
B	
C	
D	

b Devise your own decision tree to sort the numbers between 20 and 30 into prime numbers, multiples of 3 and others. Check your answer by working through each number.

2 a A new bus service is going to run from village A to village E through B, C and D. Which route should it follow to cover the shortest distance? Show clearly how you obtained your answer.

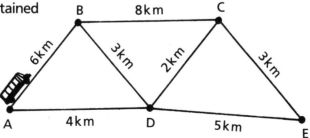

b The distance in miles between various places is shown on the diagram. What is the shortest distance between P and S? Justify your answer.

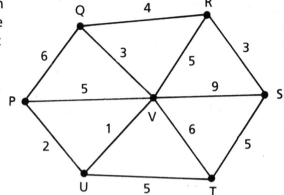

3 **a** Aziz is buying a drink for himself and one for his friend. The drinks machine gives five different types of drink as shown. Draw a table indicating the various selections he can buy. How many selections are there?

b The menu at a local restaurant is shown alongside. Arrange in a systematic way the different selections of one starter, one main course and one sweet. How many different selections can you find?

Menu

STARTER
❖
Soup
Fruit Juice
Prawn Cocktail
❖
MAIN COURSE
Lamb
Fish
Curry
❖
SWEET
Ice Cream
Sorbet
Chocolate Gateau

Answers

Section 1

1 (i) 806   (ii) 1694   (iii) 56
    (iv) 85   (v) 9288   (vi) 68

2 (i) 230 000   (ii) 21 600   (iii) 4900
    (iv) 500   (v) 44 400   (vi) 1020

3 **a** (i) 1, 2, 3, 4, 6, 12   (ii) 1, 2, 4, 7, 14, 28
    (iii) 1, 2, 4, 5, 8, 10, 20, 40   (iv) 1, 19
    (v) 1, 5, 25   (vi) 1, 2, 5, 10, 25, 50

   b 24 (Note 48 is not the answer.)

4 (i) 8   (ii) 125   (iii) 256
    (iv) 12   (v) 13   (vi) 64
    (vii) $16 \times 8 = 128$ (viii) 3   (ix) 5
    (x) 1000   (xi) 1   (xii) 40
    (xiii) 8.19 (two decimal places)
    (xiv) 2.12 (two decimal places)
    (xv) 0.913 (three decimal places)

5 **a** (i) -10 (ii) $6\frac{1}{2}$ (iii) -4
    (iv) $\frac{1}{2}$ or 0.5   (v) 14   (vi) -16
    (vii) 6

   b $1.8 - (-0.8) = 2.6$ m   (-2.6 m is wrong)

   c 23 degrees

Section 2

1 **a** $74 + 3 = 77$, $154 + 3 = 157$, $314 + 3 = 317$

   b 4, 7, 10, 13, 16 (They increase by 3 starting at 4, *or* they are all 1 greater than the multiples of 3.)

   c 7, 19, 43, 91, 187, 379, 763, 1531, 3067
      The tenth number is $2 \times 3067 + 5 = 6139$

   d (i) 9   (ii) 12   (iii) 15
      (iv) The numbers increase by 3 each time.

2 **a** (i) 12, 16, 20, 24, 28, 32
    (ii) 13, 10, 7, 4, 1, -2, -5, -8
    (iii) 2, 6, 12, 20, 30, 42, 56, 72, 90, 110

   b (i) FOR N = 1 TO 7: PRINT 2*N $-$ 1
    (ii) FOR N = 1 TO 6: PRINT 12 $-$ 2*N
    (iii) FOR N = 1 TO 5: PRINT N*N $+$ 1

Section 3

1 a (i) $\frac{12}{60} = \frac{1}{5}$ (ii) $\frac{20}{60} = \frac{1}{3}$

b (i) $1\frac{3}{5}$ (ii) $3\frac{3}{4}$ (iii) $11\frac{1}{2}$
  (iv) $6\frac{1}{3}$

c (i) $\frac{9}{5}$ (ii) $\frac{13}{8}$ (iii) $\frac{11}{4}$
  (iv) $\frac{11}{2}$

2 a 30% of £20 $= \frac{30}{100} \times 20 = £6$
    The sale price $= £20 - £6 = £14$

b (i) 40%   (ii) 75%   (iii) 87.5%
  (iv) 81.2%

c $\frac{17}{80} \times 100 = 21.25\%$

d $\frac{54}{75} \times 100 = 72\%$. She was promoted.

3 a 8 : 6 gives $8 + 6 = 14$ parts
    $£28 \div 14 = £2$
    Peter gets $8 \times £2 = £16$
    Joseph gets £12

b 3 : 2 gives $3 + 2 = 5$ parts
    $25 \div 5 = 5$ gums
    Number of black gums $= 2 \times 5 = 10$ gums

Section 4

1 a (i) 87 m   (ii) 96 mm or 9.6 cm   (iii) £9
  (iv) 33 000   (v) $11\frac{1}{2}$ (vi) £8.60

b (i) 8.63   (ii) 5.09   (iii) 0.90
  (iv) 1.04   (v) 11.40
  (vi) 1.00 (You must put the zeros.)

c (i) 680   (ii) 8.6   (iii) 810
  (iv) 1000   (v) 8.1   (vi) 16 000

2 a $A = 25$, $B = 39$ or of course $A = 39$, $B = 25$.

b Solve $x^2 = 60$, starting at roughly 7.9. The answer is 7.75.

c (i) 2.83
  (ii) 0.93

Section 5

1   (i) 2.86 m   (ii) 5.8 cm   (iii) 428 cm
     (iv) 400 mm   (v) 4.8 kg   (vi) 2800 ml
     (vii) 0.28 l   (viii) 4820 g

2   (i) 17 in   (ii) $10\frac{1}{2}$ or 10.5 ft   (iii) 18 pints
     (iv) 28 lb   (v) 80 oz   (vi) $2\frac{1}{2}$ or 2.5 lb
     (vii) 0.5 or $\frac{1}{2}$ gallon   (viii) 5 ft 4 in

3 a   (i) $6 \times 0.39 = 2.34$ in
     (ii) $400 \times 0.39 = 156$ in

   b   (i) 17.6 lb   (ii) $10 \div 22 = 4.55$ kg

4 a   (i) $10 approximately   (ii) $45 approximately
     (iii) £5.30 approximately   (iv) £62.50

   b   (i) 122 °F   (ii) 185 °F   (iii) −7 °C
     (iv) 38 °C

   c   (i) 20 (approximately)
     (ii) 50 (approximately)
     (iii) £2.25

Section 6

1 a   (i) millilitres   (ii) centimetres   (iii) tonnes
     (iv) metres   (v) metres

   b   (i) 80 cm   (ii) 64.3 g   (iii) 300 yds
     (iv) 2.8 mm   (v) 84 km   (vi) 8.6 kg

2 a $(120 \times 10) \div 8 = 150$

   b $4.3 \times 12 = 51.6$ cm
     Space left $= 150 - 51.6$
            $= 98.4$ cm

3 a   Times will be 09.10, 09.22, 09.34, 09.46, 09.58.
     Hence there are five buses.

   b   15.42 less 45 minutes $= 14.57$

   c   Times at the football ground are:
     10.23, 10.31, 10.39, 10.47, 10.55, 11.03, 11.11, 11.19,
     11.27
     This leaves the town centre at 10.49.

Section 7

1

Group	Tally	Frequency
1–5	IIII	5
6–10	IIII	5
11–15	III	3
16–20	IIII	5
21–25	II	2

2 a (i) 70   (ii) 10

b Angles for the pie chart are:
90°, 90°, 54°, 90°, 36°

c

Football	Tennis	Badminton	Snooker
17	11	22	10

3 a A: mean = 46, range = 27
B: mean = 46, range = 19
Although the averages are the same, B is more reliable.

b $(6 \times 2 + 4 \times 3) \div 10 = 2.4 \, \text{kg}$

c $(6 \times 4 + 8 \times 4) \div 12 = £4.67$

Section 8

1 Approximate values would be as follows:
(i) 0.5   (ii) 0.5–0.7   (iii) 0.2
(iv) 0.25   (v) 0.5–0.7   (vi) 0.6–0.7
(vii) 0.5   (viii) 0.2–0.4

2 a (i) A   (ii) C   (iii) B   (iv) C   (v) C

b HHH, HHT, HTH, HTT, THH, THT, TTH, TTT
Probability of two heads $= \frac{3}{8}$

c $\frac{6}{20} = \frac{3}{10}$

d

+	1	2	3	4	5	6
1	2	3	4	5	6	7
2	3	4	5	6	7	8
3	4	5	6	7	8	9
4	5	6	7	8	9	10
5	6	7	8	9	10	11
6	7	8	9	10	11	12

(i) $\frac{6}{36} = \frac{1}{6}$ (ii) $\frac{3}{36} = \frac{1}{12}$ (iii) $\frac{35}{36}$

Section 9

1 a (i) (a) acute   (b) reflex   (c) obtuse
         (d) reflex   (e) obtuse
    (ii) (a) 2   (b) 10
    (iii) (a) 3   (b) 5   (c) 7

   b (i) 126°   (ii) 130°   (iii) 40°
     (iv) $(360° - 100° - 70° - 80°) \div 2 = 55°$

2 (i) 110°, 70°, 60°   (ii) 110°, 70°, 70°
   (iii) 140°, 40°

3 a Angles are approximately 58°, 41°, 81°.

   b (i) 6.2 cm   (ii) 46°

Section 10

1 a (i) rectangle   (ii) isosceles triangle
     (iii) trapezium   (iv) square   (v) rectangle

   b There are lots of possibilities, one being (4, 3) and
     $(-3, -3)$.

   c $(-6, 2)$. This is the only answer.

2 a The overall measurements will be 18 cm by 15 cm. The
    window is 9 cm by 7 cm, etc.

   b (i) 60 cm   (ii) 0.75 km by 1.15 km

   c $a = 1.25$ m $b = 2$ m $c = 4.55$ m

Section 11

1 **a** 20 cm

   b (i) $\frac{1}{2}(2 \times 1.7) = 1.7\,m^2$
      (ii) $6 \times 1.7 = 10.2\,m^2$

   c $8 \times 2 + 4 \times 2 = 24\,cm^2$

2 **a** $192 \div (6 \times 4) = 192 \div 24 = 8\,cm$

   b $5 \times 6 \times 4 = 120$

   c (i) $\frac{1}{2} \times 1.6 \times 1.4 \times 2 = 2.24\,m^3$
      (ii) $\frac{1}{2} \times 160 \times 140 \times 200 = 2\,240\,000\,cm^3$
      To convert cubic metres to cubic centimetres you
      multiply by 1 000 000.

   d $(15 \times 12 \times 10) - (4 \times 4 \times 4) = 1800 - 64$
                              $= 1736\,cm^3$

Section 12

1 **a**   (i)   (ii)   (iii) none

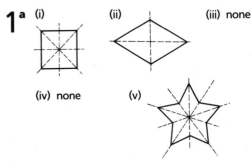

    (iv) none   (v)

   b A, D, M, T, V, W

2 **a** 3

   b

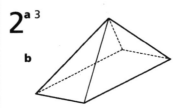

3 $\{A, C, G\}, \{E, D\}, \{I, F\}$

4   (i) order 3   (ii) order 2   (iii) order 2
    (iv) order 2   (v) no symmetry

  (i)   (ii)   (iii)   (iv)

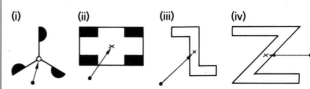

Section 13

1 a (i) $2N-5$ (ii) X^2-8 (iii) £3N

(iv) $\dfrac{(M+B+C)}{3}$ (v) x^2+y^2

b (i) 108   (ii) 34   (iii) 2

(iv) 35

c (i) 75.36 mm   (ii) 62.8 m

(iii) $50 \div 6.28 = 7.96$ km

d (i) $3.1 \times 16 = 49.6$ cm²

(ii) $\sqrt{100 \div 3.1} = 5.68$ cm

e $11 \to 41, 4 \to 13, 5 \to 17, 7 \to 25$

$y = 4x-3$

2 a (i) $8xy$ (ii) $3pq$ (iii) $6x^2$

(iv) $6H+11k$ (v) $2x^2$ (vi) $4x^2+8x$

b $p = 8x$; 52.8 cm

c $C = 6P+2R$; £120

Section 14

1 a

A	4,	8	
B	2,	6,	10
C	3,	5,	7
D	1,	9	

b See overleaf

2 a ABDCE = 14 km, ABCDE = 21 km, ADBCE = 18 km.
Hence ABDCE is the shortest route.

b PUVRS = 11 miles

3 a

	O	L	C	A	B
O	×	×	×	×	×
L	×	×	×	×	×
C	×	×	×	×	×
A	×	×	×	×	×
B	×	×	×	×	×

25 possible selections

b 27 possible selections

1 ^b

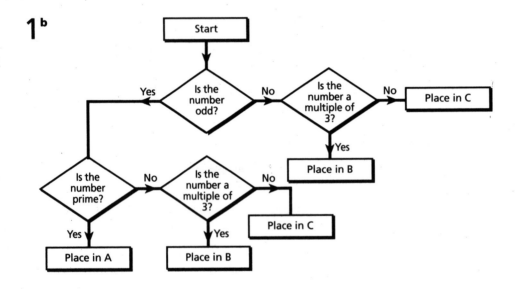

Sample Test Paper

1 (i) A contractor has to move a consignment of 58 tons of scrap metal from a building site using this lorry. How many times will the lorry have to visit the site? (Show all your working.)

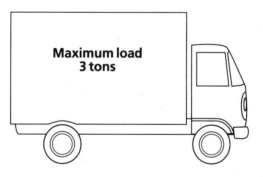

Maximum load
3 tons

(ii) If he wants to make no more than 11 visits, what would be the smallest whole number that could appear on the load plate? (Show all your working.)

2 There are different ways of estimating probabilities:
Method A: Use equally likely outcomes.
Method B: Look back at data.
Method C: Survey or experiment to collect data.
   Look at the following situations and say whether you would use method A, method B or method C to estimate the probability.

   (i) The probability that a pupil chosen at random from your class likes tennis.
   (ii) The probability of drawing an ace from a complete pack of playing cards.
   (iii) The probability that it will rain tomorrow.
   (iv) The probability that a certain volcano will erupt next year.
   (v) The probability that Tim will be late for school tomorrow.

3

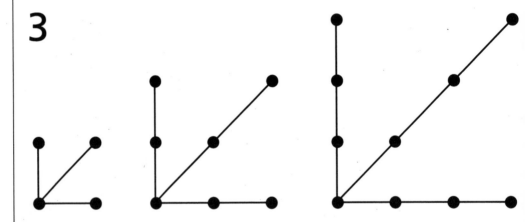

   (i) Look at the patterns shown above, and then complete the next two entries in the table.

Pattern	1	2	3	4	5
No. of dots	4	7	10		

   (ii) The rule for all these patterns is given by the following:

   Number of pattern N —[× ?]—[+ 1]——→ number of dots D

   What is missing?
   (iii) Write the rule using algebra.

4 The diagram shows part of a design for a stained glass window, with measurements in metric units. What do you think those units are?

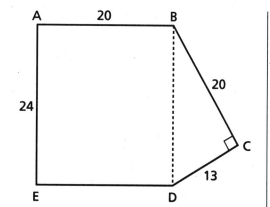

With these units, find:
(i) the area of the rectangular part ABDE;
(ii) the area of the triangular part BCD;
(iii) the total area ABCDE.
If angle DBC = 35°, find angle EDC, giving reasons for your answer.

5 For the following shapes, mark any centres of rotational symmetry, and any mirror lines of symmetry.

(i)

(ii)

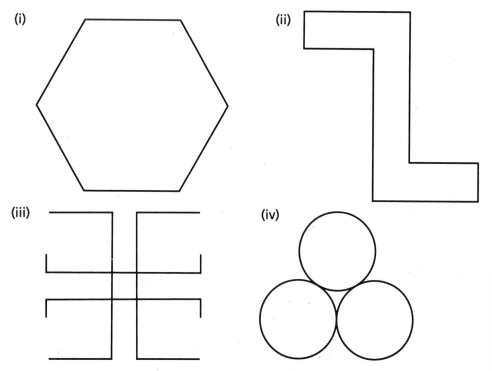

(iii)

(iv)

For those shapes with rotational symmetry, state the order of rotational symmetry.

6 A map has been drawn to a scale of 1:400 000. Find the distance in kilometres between two villages that are 8 cm apart on the map.

7 A group of factory workers were told that if they took a 20% pay cut, they would be able to keep their jobs. Afsal normally earned £184 per week.

    (i) How much would he earn in a week after the pay cut?

    (ii) Assuming he is paid 52 weeks a year, and he decided to take a part-time job, how much would he have to earn in a year, to make up the wages he will lose?

8 Damian bought a train set in the sale. It was originally priced at £84. How much did he pay for it in the sale?

Big reductions 1/4 off marked prices

9 The given map shows the streets where Amy does her paper round.

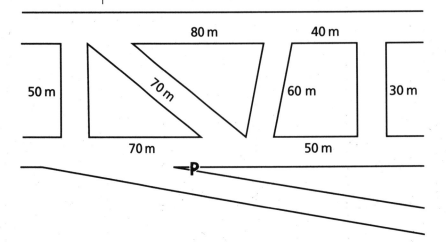

(i) Draw a network to represent the map.

(ii) If Amy starts and finishes at the papershop and delivers in each road, what is the shortest total journey she can make?

10 Draw on graph paper a set of axes, with x from -10 to 10 and y from -10 to 10.

    (i) Plot A(4, 0), B(6, 2) and D(2, 2). If ABCD is a square, what are the coordinates of C?

    (ii) Plot P(-10, -4), Q(4, -4) and R(0, 6). If each unit on the graph paper is 1 cm, what is the area of the triangle PQR?

11   (i) List all factors of the number 64.

    (ii) What are the prime factors of 64?

  (iii) Express 64 as a power of 2.

12 Find the angles marked with a letter in the following diagram. Give reasons for your answers.

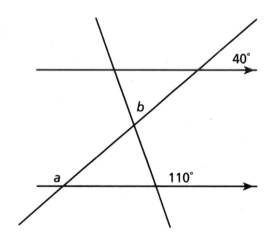

13 Use a trial and improvement method to find $\sqrt{18}$ correct to two decimal places.

14 The bar graph shows the amount of pocket money received by the pupils in 9X2.

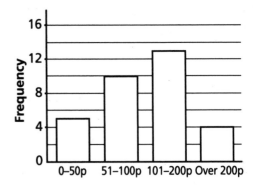

(i) How many pupils received between 50p and £1?

(ii) How many pupils were given more than 50p?

(iii) How many pupils are there in 9X2?

15 (i) Draw a conversion graph to convert French francs (fr.) to pounds, given that 19fr. = £2. Label the horizontal axis from £(0–10) and the vertical axis from (0–100)fr.

(ii) Use your graph to find:

   (a) the number of francs for £6.50;

   (b) the value of 85fr. in pounds;

   (c) the number of francs for £143;

   (d) the number of pounds for 450fr.

Explain clearly how you obtained your answers to parts (c) and (d).

Solutions

1

(i) $58 \div 3$

$$3\overline{)58} \quad \frac{19}{} \text{ remainder } 1$$

$$\begin{array}{r} 19 \\ 3\overline{)58} \\ \underline{3} \\ 28 \\ \underline{27} \\ 1 \end{array}$$ remainder 1

20 journeys are necessary (not 19).

(ii) $58 \div 11$ gives 5 remainder 3.
Hence the load must show at least 6 tons.

2 (i) C (ii) A (iii) B (iv) B
(v) C

3

(i)

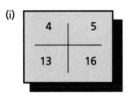

(ii) $\times 3$ (iii) $D = 3N + 1$

4 Probably centimetres, but it could be millimetres if it is a
small part of a window.
  (i) $20 \times 24 = 480 \text{ cm}^2$
  (ii) $\frac{1}{2} \times 20 \times 13 = 130 \text{ cm}^2$
  (iii) $480 + 130 = 610 \text{ cm}^2$

$\angle BDC = 180° - 35° - 90° = 55°$
(angle sum of triangle)

$\therefore \quad \angle EDC = 90° + 55° = 145°$

5

(i)

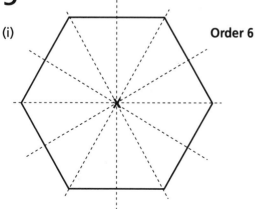

Order 6

(ii)

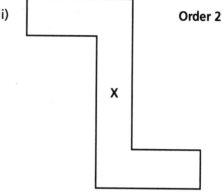

Order 2

(iii)

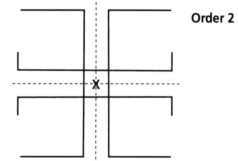

Order 2

(iv)

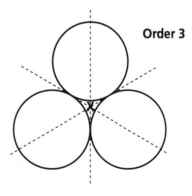

Order 3

6 400 000 cm = 4 km
Hence 1 cm on the map represents 4 km

∴ 8 cm is 8 × 4 = 32 km

7 (i) 20% of £184 = $\frac{20}{100}$ × 184

= £36.80

Hence Afsal will earn £184 − £36.80 = £147.20.
(ii) He would need to earn 52 × £36.80 = £1913.60.

8 To find $\frac{1}{4}$ of £84, divide by 4:

£84 ÷ 4 = £21

The sale price = £84 − £21 = £63.

9 (i)

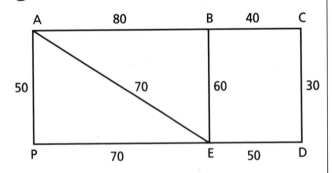

Make sure the distances are marked, and that each node is given a letter.
(ii) You need to avoid going along the longer roads twice if possible, and also twice along BCDE. The best route is PABEDCBEAP, a distance of

50 + 80 + 60 + 50 + 30 + 40 + 60 + 70 + 50 = 490 m

10

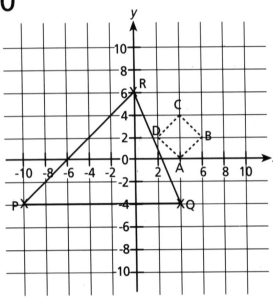

(i) C is (4, 4).
(ii) Using area = $\frac{1}{2}$ base × height
= $\frac{1}{2}$ × 14 × 10
= 70 cm²

11 (i) 1, 2, 4, 8, 16, 32, 64
(ii) 2 is the *only* prime factor.
(iii) 64 = 2⁶   (2 to the power 6)

12

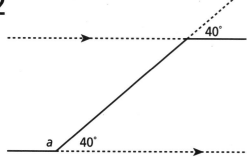

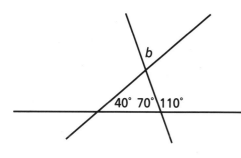

$a = 180° − 40°$
$= 140°$
(Corresponding angles and angles on a straight line)

$b = 180° − 40° − 70°$
$= 70°$
(Angle sum of triangle)

13 $4^2 = 16$ and $5^2 = 25$, hence $\sqrt{18}$ lies between 4 and 5.

  1st try: $4.2^2 = 17.64$ too low
  2nd try: $4.25^2 = 18.0625$ just too high
  3rd try: $4.24^2 = 17.9776$ too low but nearer

Hence $\sqrt{18} = 4.24$ to two decimal places.

14 The bar graph can be summarised as follows:

Group	0–50	51–100	101–200	Over 200
Frequency	5	10	13	4

This makes the question much easier to answer.
  (i) 10 pupils
  (ii) $10 + 13 + 4 = 27$ pupils
  (iii) $5 + 10 + 13 + 4 = 32$ pupils

15 (i)

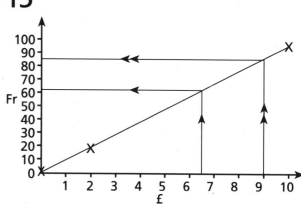

  (ii) (a) 62fr. (approx.)
     (b) £9 (approx.)
     (c) £10 = 95fr.

       So £140 = 95×14 = 1330fr.
        also £3 = 28fr.

       The total is $1330 + 28 = 1358$fr. i.e. 1360fr. approximately.
     (d) 100fr. = £10.50 approximately, so

       400fr. = $4 \times$ £10.50 = £42
        50fr. = £5 approximately

       Hence 450fr. = £47 approximately.